G000279757

LAND FOR A LOST GENERATION

LAND FOR A LOST GENERATION

Michael J. Richards

ARTHUR H. STOCKWELL LTD
Torrs Park, Ilfracombe, Devon, EX34 8BA
Established 1898
www.ahstockwell.co.uk

© *Michael J. Richards, 2021*
First published in Great Britain, 2021

The moral rights of the author have been asserted.

All rights reserved.
No part of this publication may be reproduced
or transmitted in any form or by any means,
electronic or mechanical, including photocopy,
recording, or any information storage and
retrieval system, without permission
in writing from the copyright holder.

British Library Cataloguing-in-Publication Data.
A catalogue record for this book is available
from the British Library.

This is a work of fiction. Names, characters, places and incidents are
the product of the author's imagination and any resemblance to actual
persons, living or dead, events or locales, is purely coincidental.

ISBN 978-0-7223-5120-8
Printed in Great Britain by
Arthur H. Stockwell Ltd
Torrs Park   Ilfracombe
Devon EX34 8BA

CONTENTS

CHAPTER 1

ALMA MATER

Endacott Ladies' College is perhaps a misnomer inasmuch as it is not an institution for young women, but a fee-paying school for girls. It was founded by Ernestine Endacott, a Victorian educationalist who championed feminine causes and had the good fortune, through a substantial legacy, to put her theories into practice. Thus it came to pass that a red-brick pile mushroomed amongst the woodland and pasture of the Sussex Weald.

This unlikely incursion into the countryside was completed in 1863, with Miss Endacott installing herself as its first headmistress. A bust of this formidable lady is unmissable as one passes through the main entrance. Five years ago the school celebrated its golden anniversary – an occasion witnessed by me as a new entrant to its student body.

Perhaps I should introduce myself. I am Vera Stansfield. There is nothing particularly remarkable about me. I was born in 1900 as the nineteenth century staggered to its close under the shadow of Britain at war in South Africa. Now that I have celebrated my eighteenth birthday our country is once more embroiled in conflict and has been for nearly four years. This is a salient time in my life, for we are in July and the summer term is drawing to its close. As an upper sixth-former I am about to leave school and be cast with my contemporaries upon an unsuspecting world.

Geographically, Endacott is not so very far from horrors of the Western Front, yet within its cloistered walls we seem to be as remote from that conflagration as it is possible to get. Boys' schools, I know, have memorial boards listing past pupils who have fallen in battle. We girls are spared that sobering reminder

– or at least we were until it was announced during assembly a few days ago that Edith Nixon, one of our alumnae, was killed by a shell which hit her ambulance as she was ferrying wounded men from a field dressing station. So Endacott is to have its own memorial board. Mercifully, there will be only one name on it, and we can but pray there will be no additions.

Apart from this grisly episode, Endacott's only concession to the war is that we make and send items to soldiers at the front. We knit woollen gloves, scarves and balaclavas, and write letters of gratitude and hope which, I am given to understand, reduce some battle-hardened men to tears. Sometimes we receive replies, only to learn subsequently that their authors have perished; and then it is our turn to be upset.

I share a room at the end of a corridor with two other girls: Dorothy Postgate and Lilian Cairns. Dorothy – or Dotty, as we call her – is a jolly person and certainly not dotty by reputation. She cannot by any stretch of the imagination be regarded as fat, but she is, shall we say, amply provided for. Lilian is beautiful. I do not think I am bad-looking, yet I cannot compare with Lilian's elegance and vivacity. She is also highly talented and is always chosen for the lead roles in school plays. Her fine soprano voice is admired and she delights us with her solo performances. Lilian wishes to become a professional actress and singer, and she has already secured a place at a London drama and music academy. I wish her well.

Dotty and I are uncertain about our futures. It seems that Endacott has merely prepared us to become embraced in the arms of holy matrimony. We can both cook and sew to a reasonable standard. I can play the piano and I am quite good at English literature, largely because I am a hopeless romantic who has read all of Jane Austen's novels. Sometimes I think that I might like to be a writer, but I am not sure whether I should be good enough or have the necessary discipline. Dotty is matronly and ideally suited to motherhood. If she has to earn her own living, I think she would make a very good nurse or children's nanny.

All this speculation about our adult life, however, is brought into stark reality. A few days before school breaks up for the summer vacation, our Headmistress, Miss Buckmaster, calls the upper sixth into the assembly hall.

"Girls," she begins, "It has always been my policy to address those of you who are due to leave us at the end of term. Two years ago, in the wake of the first day of the Battle of the Somme, I changed the tone of my message of goodwill for your futures. It became evident to me then – and my view has hardened ever since – that this war has killed and continues to kill thousands upon thousands of our young men. This is the generation from whom you might expect to secure husbands. The blunt truth is that, no matter when this conflict comes to its conclusion, there will not be enough eligible men to go round for girls of your age. I should be failing in my duty if I did not apprise you of this unpalatable fact. You must all accept the very real possibility that you will spend your entire adult lives as spinsters. I cannot hide from you the prospect that the prettiest girls will have the best chances. You owe it to yourselves to make as much provision for your futures as you can with particular regard to a career. Some of you, I know, have already done this, but there is no room for complacency. Do not imagine that the cessation of hostilities will bring a large influx of men back to this country, all wanting to sweep you off your feet to a life of domestic bliss. They will be relatively few in number, and some of them will be damaged in mind or body and will be very different from the boys who volunteered in a wave of patriotism and hope. If I can be of any assistance in helping you to secure a position of employment, or a place at an institute of learning, then my door is always open. It only remains for me to wish you every success as you embark upon your lives in the outside world."

As we emerge from the hall our dispositions are in marked contrast to the chatter which usually accompanies an exodus of this nature. An eerie silence has descended upon us as we digest the full import of Miss Buckmaster's address. It is not that the implications of war have not crossed our minds hitherto, but the grave tones in which our headmistress has delivered the awful truth have cut through us like a knife.

I can see that some girls are on the verge of tears and most faces are ashen. There is one notable exception. Millicent Harper is the school swot to end all school swots. She has won a scholarship to read classics at Girton College, Cambridge. I do not begrudge Millicent her success. She is the plainest of girls, with thick-lensed spectacles. I suspect she inured herself long ago to the notion that no young man was ever likely to woo her. So here is nemesis for more attractive females of my generation and retribution for those whose assets are confined to the cerebral.

Dotty, Lilian and I sit on the ends of our beds and stare into oblivion. We do so probably for no longer than thirty seconds, but it seems like a millennium before Dotty breaks the silence.

"Well, what do you think of that?"

"Bit of a squashed tomato," Lilian suggests.

"It's all right for you," laments Dotty. "You're pretty and have a career lined up. You'll have no trouble finding a husband; and even if you don't, you'll earn a good living."

I try to deflect the aura of depression which is threatening to envelop us.

"There's no point in our feeling sorry for ourselves. Think of what our poor men are going through. This is a picnic compared to their situation."

So we bottle up our thoughts on the subject as far as interaction is concerned, yet I find my mind occupied by little else.

The last day of term arrives and there is the usual buzz and bustle associated with being released from an institution and gaining a freedom not enjoyed since Easter. Some parents have come by a variety of horse-drawn or motorised conveyances to collect their daughters and luggage. Most girls, however, make their way on foot to the village railway station. All this activity has been familiar to me for some years now; but of course, for those of us departing for the last time there is an added poignancy. We are saying goodbye to friends and colleagues whom we may never see again. It is an anticlimax, a sadness, possibly even a fear of the unknown beyond. My two room-mates and I resolve to keep in touch and we make reference to the Old Girls' Association and school reunions. This has cheered me a little. I hate goodbyes and dread the possibility of their permanence.

CHAPTER 2

THE REAL WORLD

During the spring Germany had launched an offensive in a desperate attempt to force a victory in France. There was a fear that the Hun would break through our lines. Field Marshal Haig said that with our backs to the wall and believing in the justice of our cause each one of us must fight to the end. The German advance, however, stalled and ran out of steam.

I learn now from August newspapers that we have launched an offensive of our own at Amiens under Sir Henry Rawlinson. He was the general who presided over the Somme disaster of 1916, when 20,000 of our men were slaughtered on the first day of the battle. Fortunately, it seems that our military leaders have learnt a great deal about modern warfare since then. It only appals me that the fees of such an education have been paid in the blood of so many others. On this occasion the wisdom of a co-ordinated attack involving artillery, tanks, infantry and aircraft has been employed with considerable success. There is now an expectation, particularly with the Americans operational in France, that we can press on to ultimate victory.

If only this optimism is well founded. The stalemate and attrition of trench warfare have blighted so many lives for so long. My enduring regret is that many more of our men may have to die before this insanity is terminated. Then, if we do win the war, can we also win the peace?

My father is a country solicitor and my mother runs our home as his dutiful wife. We live in Sussex, within twenty miles of Endacott. I have a younger brother, Edwin, who is just twelve years old and therefore likely to be spared the horrors of military conflict.

Since returning home I have exercised my mind more fully about my future. There is the short-term future and the long term. While our country is engaged in hostilities it is the short term which should take precedence. I have to make my contribution to the war effort. I have done my bit as a schoolgirl, knitting and sending warm clothing with letters of encouragement to the front; now I must participate as an adult, even though, as my parents constantly remind me, I am but an adolescent. What can I do? Not much, probably. I am too young to become a VAD like Edith Nixon and run the risk of sacrificing myself. Of course, boys of my age are volunteering for active service and, once nineteen, can be conscripted. People, however, keep telling me it is different for girls.

A chance conversation with a friend of my mother's provides a possible solution. Within a bicycle ride of our home a convalescent camp for wounded soldiers has been constructed. There are rows of wooden huts augmented by several tents – an emergency measure to accommodate the ever burgeoning number of casualties. The largest hut, to which the kitchen is attached, serves as a room for dining and recreational purposes. Inside there is an upright piano which no one can play properly. My mother's friend tells me how helpful it would be if a competent pianist can be found.

Endacott has a strong music department, and much of my time there was spent learning to play the instrument in question. Thus proficiency in this regard came to be what Victorians might have called "one of my accomplishments". I suspect that Miss Ernestine Endacott had in mind a young lady entertaining dinner guests in a private residence with classical selections on the pianoforte. One can scarcely imagine what her thoughts would have been on one of her alumnae plonking out popular numbers in front of raucous battle-scarred troops in a wooden hut!

Nevertheless, it comes to pass that this unusual activity provides me with an opportunity to do something worthwhile. Each day I arm myself with a sheaf of sheet music and cycle to the camp, where my material reward comes in the form of luncheon, during which I share conversation with my audience.

I play the songs which soldiers like to sing, such as 'Tipperary' and 'Pack up your Troubles'. Their favourite is 'Mademoiselle from Armentières', to which they have their own words – lyrics that make me blush with embarrassment. They know my reaction and sing all the louder with mischievous grins on their faces. Despite their crudities I am full of admiration for them. Some are amputees, yet their spirits are almost inexplicably high. It breaks my heart to see their broken bodies. How small and inadequate I feel in comparison! But these poor fellows, who have given so much, call me their 'angel'. I am no angel, and when I have a moment to myself I break down in tears.

In addition to playing the piano I help other lady volunteers by handing out books and magazines to the wounded men, all of whom wear blue uniforms. What they want more than anything, however, is for me to talk and listen to them. A female voice and presence remind them of home and for what they fought. They show me photographs of their families. These include baby sons and daughters whom they are yet to see in person. Some soldiers, whose relatives live not too far distant, receive visitors. When a wife sees her amputee husband for the first time it can be and usually is a most distressing experience. I try to comfort these women as best I can.

"How is he going to provide for us now?" is a familiar question which I cannot answer, particularly when someone like a tram driver in civilian life has lost his hands.

I receive a letter from Lilian. There is such demand for entertainment in London that she has been plucked from her drama and music academy to be given a small part in a West End show. I am so pleased for her. She is doing what she wants to do in a world where so many are obliged to do what they least wish.

I write back and offer my congratulations. I mention that her success must preclude her from getting any spare time. To my surprise she replies quickly, saying that generously she is given two free days each fortnight. I have a brainwave and suggest that she visits me during her next break. To my delight, she agrees and I invite Dotty to come too.

Dotty is working at a shell-shock hospital in Surrey. It is a most heart-rending and depressing experience for her. Apart from the drudgery of her duties, such as scrubbing floors and emptying bedpans, it is almost impossible to build any rapport with the poor, wretched patients. Some of them shake uncontrollably, while others just stare at the wall. Now and again a deeply disturbed fellow will begin shouting and try to escape through a window or crawl hopelessly about the floor. I see the physical scars of war and Dotty the psychological. She is only too pleased to accept my invitation to give herself the rest and recuperation she needs.

So the three of us are to be reunited, albeit briefly. I wait on the platform of our village station one morning during late September. A puff of smoke in the distance tells me the train is approaching. It soon steams in and comes to rest with the brake pump of its locomotive panting as though to remind everyone of the huge effort expended in getting here. Only one carriage door opens on to our short rural platform, and I see Dotty and Lilian about to come towards me as I do to them. It is only two months since we last met, but it seems to be a lifetime. This feeling is accentuated by the fact that then we were schoolgirls and now we are, to all intents and purposes, women.

Lilian is resplendent in a bright-green outfit with feathers. She looks every inch the showgirl, and I am almost jealous. Dotty understandably appears somewhat careworn, but soon returns to her old ebullient self. We exchange stories, and to my delight Lilian volunteers to sing to my piano accompaniment at the convalescent camp. I point out that she is supposed to be having a rest, but she dismisses my concern through reminding me that her expected audience has given so much and she owes them at least a little in return. I am so glad that Lilian has not allowed success to go to her head. If she becomes really famous, then I think she will be able to handle the pressure without relinquishing her good heart.

Today is supposed to be one of my days off from the camp, but Lilian's generosity has impelled me to reciprocate. The autumnal weather is wonderful and we sit in garden deckchairs after lunch, drinking tea before setting out on bicycles for our destination. Lilian borrows my mother's machine while Dotty has the most precarious ride on Edwin's cycle, which is smaller and possesses a lady's inconvenience of a crossbar.

So we are to give an unexpected performance, and the boys in blue make their way into the large hut, some on crutches and others with the aid of wheelchairs. The walking wounded wait politely for the less ambulant to be settled before they find a seat themselves. I decide to give Lilian a big introduction.

"Right, boys – you weren't expecting to see me today, but we have a special guest with us. She is a star from the West End stage in London and has just arrived by train specially to be with you. Will you please give a very warm welcome to Miss Lilian Cairns!"

The soldiers cheer and applaud enthusiastically. I do not doubt they are besotted by her beauty and attire. I take up my usual position at the piano and turn the sheet music to the first song which Lilian has chosen. 'Roses of Picardy,' written only two years ago by Haydn Wood, has taken London by storm and it is now up to Lilian to do it justice.

Whenever I have performed here before there has always been an undercurrent of sound from the audience, but, as I play the prelude and Lilian prepares to come in at the appropriate moment, one could hear a pin drop were it not for the piano.

I always knew Lilian could sing well at school, but I never dreamt that in such a short space of time she could elevate her ability to the stunning level she is now attaining. Her control is exquisite. She can hold a note and allow her voice to rise or fall as the best interpretation of the tune demands. My playing is but incidental to the performance. If she were to sing unaccompanied it would be just as beautiful, probably better. This is professional standard par excellence. A mere two months of intensive work in the metropolis has produced a future star indeed – and when I think that singing is but one of her talents!

When the song is finished I look up from the music sheet and observe that nearly every soldier has tears streaming down his face. They have known unspeakable horrors, and now they have seen and heard something beautiful which they could not have contemplated at this remote camp in rural Sussex. A few poignant seconds elapse before everyone bursts into loud applause with shouts of "Encore!"

It is not only singing to this high level that Lilian has learnt, but also how to respond to an appreciative audience. She beams broadly and bows in gratitude. The soldiers demand the same song again, and she is only too willing to perform it. She signals her instructions to me, whereupon we repeat our efforts to another rapturous reception.

Our next song is Ivor Novello's 'Keep the Home Fires Burning', written in the autumn of 1914. In late 1915 the *Daily Mail* reported that this 'has become the Battle Hymn of the Great War'. When the boys in blue ask for an encore Lilian agrees provided they join in. They need little encouragement. So, with Lilian leading, the wooden hut reverberates to its rafters. If anyone wanted a morale booster in this place, then he has it in Lilian.

She now takes a bold and very risky step by asking for requests. We do not want to disappoint anybody, so Lilian has to hope she knows the song and I have to hope that I have the music to play it. Fortunately, all is well and finally we take a rest to walk around with Dotty to talk with our wounded heroes. Lilian is in her element and the soldiers cannot get enough of her. I speak briefly with Dotty before the men start attracting our attention again.

"Look at her, Dotty – she's really got it, hasn't she?"

"Yes, I never realised she could be that good."

As we cycle back to my parents' house I cannot begin to thank Lilian enough.

"This bicycle ride has got to be the worst way of expressing my gratitude, Lilian. After a performance like that you deserve a motor car to whisk you away to the Ritz or somewhere."

"Don't imagine, Vera," she replies philosophically, "that the theatre is as glamorous as many may think. It's jolly hard work and I'm still learning my craft."

CHAPTER 3

DAVID

October arrives and there is encouraging news from the Western Front. A series of co-ordinated attacks by the Allies along the Hindenburg Line has forced the Germans to retreat. The Americans under General Pershing are involved in large numbers near the Argonne Forest and River Meuse. Is this the beginning of the end for our enemy? One can only hope. Everybody seems to be asking, "Will the horror of this dreadful war never end?"

As though providence wishes to punish mankind for the foolishness of its conflict, an influenza epidemic has spread across the globe. It seems to have begun in the Near East. Having reached Central Europe in August, it is now with us. So virulent is this outbreak that, like the war, it is killing large numbers of people. Now even within our own shores we fear death. Lilian writes to tell me that she and many others walk about London with their faces covered lest they become infected.

Dotty comes to stay for a weekend. Lilian's work schedule does not permit her to join us. It is not Lilian, however, whom I am worried about save for the influenza issue. She is happy, motivated and successful. Dotty on the other hand is being ground down by her duties in Surrey. It is valuable work yet utterly debilitating. The whole ethos of the hospital is one of hopelessness and containment. It is no place for a girl of eighteen, but how can I tell her that she ought to leave? What I am able to do is invite her to Sussex and try to cheer her up.

There is to be a dance with refreshments in the village hall, and I think this is exactly what Dotty needs. No doubt there will be a dearth of young men, but everyone is used to that in Britain at present. The dance is in aid of local war widows, so it is likely to be well attended. Dotty is looking forward to it, and this pleases me greatly.

We are indeed fortunate to have a village hall. Many communities are without them. Ours is a corrugated-iron structure built and donated by a local landowner to mark the coronation of King George V in 1911. It is soon pulsating with activity as the dance gets under way. Dotty and I are fully engaged with partners who are old enough to be our fathers, or even our grandfathers. We take it all in good part, but, when there is an interlude to give the small band a rest, we scan the room in search for someone a little younger.

It seems to be a fruitless quest, and then I notice him. I can scarcely believe it: a young army officer sitting at a table and gazing around as though he is waiting just for me. He has three pips and two rings on his sleeve, so he is a captain. Frustration – Dotty has seen him too.

"I saw him first," she avers.

"How do you make that out?" I query.

"All right – I'll toss you for him."

"Done."

Dotty produces a penny.

"Call," she demands.

"Heads."

Oh dear – it is a disappointment for Dotty, whom I was trying to hearten by bringing her here.

"Look," I tell her, "you go on. I don't want you to lose out."

"No," she insists, "you won fairly and squarely, so you get first try."

I feel a bit mean, yet I am lured to this dashing young man. If he is not interested in me, then good luck to Dotty. I approach the table where he is sitting and introduce myself rather boldly.

"You must think this very forward of me," I confess.

"I'm David Coulthurst; and no, I don't think you're very forward. This war is changing everything. Gone are the days when a young lady would not speak to a gentleman without first having been introduced by a third person – not that I consider myself to be a gentleman exactly. You don't have a chaperon either, do you? The old order changeth, blown away on the fields of France like so much else."

"I was going to break another convention and ask you for the next dance."

"Well, that is unusual and very flattering coming from one as pretty as you."

I blush uncontrollably.

"So," I reply expectantly, "will you partner me?"

"I'm afraid I can't."

I feel like a pricked balloon.

"Oh," I sigh, barely able to conceal my disappointment, "I'm sorry. I didn't realise you're booked with someone else."

"I'm not – it's just that I can't dance."

"Can't dance? A young officer like you! Of course you can dance! All officers are supposed to be gentlemen and able to dance, aren't they?"

"I didn't say I don't know how to. I just said I *can't*."

"I don't understand."

At this point he holds up a walking stick previously hidden by the table.

"I've got this, you see. It's as much as I can do to walk more than a few yards in one go without taking a rest."

I wish the floor would open up beneath my feet so that I could sink ignominiously from sight.

"Oh, you've been wounded."

"Afraid so – piece of shrapnel in the lower left leg. They got it out, but let's just say I'll never play cricket again. I expect you'll want to ask somebody else now."

To my shame, I hesitate. I need to say something quickly.

"No, I don't want to ask anyone else."

"You'd better sit down, then."

So I sit opposite him and we converse copiously. He tells me that he is the son of a tenant farmer. I enquire whether he could have claimed exemption from military service on the grounds of reserved occupation. He says that he could have done, but both he and his elder brother, Vere, were determined to enlist at the outbreak of war, nearly two years before conscription began. Vere was not so lucky. He perished last year in the mud of Passchendaele, the Third Battle of Ypres. His body was never recovered. I cannot speak.

David goes on to say that his hard-working father lost the will to live after this and was himself dead before the new year dawned. So his distraught mother is trying to keep the farm going and prays for her younger son's safe return.

"The problem is", he admits sadly, "that with a gammy leg I'm not likely to be much use on a farm now. I could give orders to the men and handle the paperwork, but that would just about be it."

I can see that he is really depressed and, in the absence of anything more constructive to say, I enquire whether I may fetch him some refreshments. He nods gratefully. As I queue for sustenance Dotty buttonholes me and suggests that I have been given the brush-off. I deny this and relate what has happened.

"Poor boy!" she concedes.

"Yes, Dotty, and he needs someone to talk to. So I think I should help him; and if I help myself too, then that's a bonus."

Dotty – bless her – wishes me well and I return to David with a tray of sandwiches and lemonade. He has a healthy appetite, which is encouraging, and he seems willing to tell me all as though it is some cathartic process.

It transpires that he and Vere began their army service as private soldiers, advancing through the ranks to earn their commissions.

"There would have been no such opportunity in peacetime," David reveals. "The officer corps is reserved for the privileged classes as a rule, but when nearly everyone is getting killed the powers that be are forced to start scraping the barrel."

"You shouldn't put yourself down," I tell him.

"I think you're a good egg," he responds, "but I just explain things as they are."

I detect a cynicism in his demeanour, yet how can I blame him in view of what he has been through? Despite all these dreadful experiences I can see he has a concern for others. In particular he is worried about his mother.

"I don't know what's going to happen about the farm," he confesses. "My mother cannot continue as she is for much longer, and I don't really see how I can help."

"When will this awful war finish?" I ask.

"How long is a piece of string?" he answers rhetorically. "I suppose it's just a question of how long the Hun wants to go on fighting. We've blockaded them, so if they're starving they'll pack up. They're also continuing to retreat, and they can only run so far."

"So you think we're going to win?"

"Probably, but what exactly should we win: pride, influence, wealth? I don't think so. When the final audit is taken we shall ask how could we all have been so stupid?"

He enquires whether I should like to visit the farm and meet his mother. I say that I should be delighted. I introduce him to Dotty.

"We're old school friends," I explain.

"Which school?" David queries.

"Endacott Ladies' College," reveals Dotty.

"Well, that puts you both in a higher social bracket than I am."

"Nonsense!" I declare. "What was that you were telling me about the old order changing?"

David ponders a response.

"Yes, there will be changes," he asserts. "I just hope they'll all be for the better."

CHAPTER 4

DOWN ON THE FARM

Vine's Farm extends to about 150 acres and it forms part of the Cloudsley Estate owned by the Fifth Earl of Cloudsley. David's family have been the tenants here for two generations. The farm is a twenty-minute cycle ride from my parents' home, and I pay my first visit to the Coulthursts one afternoon just days following the fundraising dance.

Despite the time of year it is not raining, and this gives me an opportunity to survey the steading at my leisure before presenting myself at the front door of the farmhouse. It is a mixed agricultural enterprise: arable, dairy and other livestock. The cows – a herd of dairy shorthorns – are already winter-housed to protect the pastures from being poached. There are well-stocked pigsties, while free-range hens appear from every nook and cranny before disappearing again. I spy sheep grazing in the distance. Pest control seems to be vested in an army of cats, which stick together and keep a suspicious eye upon me. A pair of shire horses poke their heads beyond stable doors in expectation that I might bring them oats to supplement their hay.

The buildings appear to be well maintained, and there exists a general tidiness about the place which has often been absent in other farms I have observed. The farmhouse dates from the mid nineteenth century – local brick topped with a slate roof. It is surrounded on three sides by horse chestnut trees. I can imagine Vere and David as boys playing conkers during autumn. How innocent they must have looked, and no one then could have predicted the tragedy which lay ahead!

I knock on the front door. There is a delay before David answers, leaning awkwardly on his walking stick. He is out of uniform, dressed in a thick woollen jumper with a high neck, not unlike the type sailors wear.

"I'm sorry I can't get to the door any quicker," he laments.

I tell him that he has nothing for which to apologise. He shows me into the parlour – a welcoming room where a log fire is burning in the grate.

"I trust it's not too hot in here for you," he says. "Perhaps we're a little extravagant in heating the house, but on a farm there's always plenty of wood about."

"Not at all – it's all very cosy."

A middle-aged lady enters. David introduces me to his mother. The stress of responsibility and bereavement is clearly etched in her countenance. She is polite, but unsmiling. I get the impression that she has not smiled for many months. The three of us take tea together. Mrs Coulthurst has help in the house in the person of Rosie, a rather simple village girl who appears willing yet in need of direction. She acts as our waitress.

"We require three teaspoons, Rosie, as there are three of us today," advises Mrs Coulthurst. "You do take sugar, don't you, Miss Stansfield?"

"A little – yes, please. Can you still get sugar with all the shortages?"

"We save it for special occasions. One good thing about being farmers is that we have several kinds of food with which we can barter. It also helps that David is in the army. I always get him to wear his uniform when we're in need of something."

I smile benignly although Mrs Coulthurst remains stony-faced.

"David tells me you're an Endacott girl."

"Yes."

"What does your father do?"

"He's a solicitor."

I begin to feel that I am being interviewed, and it would seem to be the case.

"Have you embarked upon any sort of career?"

"No, Mrs Coulthurst, but I play piano for convalescent soldiers at the nearby camp."

"So you are a musician?"

"Well, not professionally, you understand. I learnt to play and read music at school."

"Yes, I suppose they would teach that kind of thing in a place like Endacott."

"Oh, yes, a wide range of subjects is taught. Even riding was offered in the sixth form before the war, but then the army came and took all the horses away."

David's mother takes a sip of tea.

"Can you ride, Miss Stansfield?"

"No, worst luck; I didn't enter the sixth form until 1916. All the stables were emptied long before then."

"How very irritating for you!"

I am unsure whether to detect a whiff of sarcasm directed against me at this point.

"I shouldn't complain though, should I, Mrs Coulthurst? We have to give precedence to our men at the front."

I sense that I have struck a raw nerve with my hostess, who probably wishes not to be reminded of activities in France.

"Will you take another scone, Miss Stansfield? They are home-made. Rosie helped me to make them, didn't you, Rosie?"

A grin develops on the girl's face.

"Rosie, go and make another pot of tea."

"But there's still some in here, Mrs Coulthurst."

"It's stewed. Go and make a fresh pot."

"Yes, Mrs Coulthurst."

Rosie departs in the direction of the kitchen. David's mother looks me hard in the face.

"I'm not one to beat about the bush, Miss Stansfield. Have you any idea what it would be like to take on a crippled man?"

"Mother, really!"

"David, be quiet! Well, Miss Stansfield?"

I hardly know where to put myself. I know I am blushing and cannot control it. I am also unable to speak. Mrs Coulthurst, however, is quite capable of speaking and desirous of doing so.

"David has told me he has fallen for you."

"Mother, I—"

24

"David, I told you to be quiet! Miss Stansfield, you are very young."

"I am eighteen."

"Precisely. David is twenty-four and knows his own mind. Isn't it true that you only left school three months past?"

"Yes, but I could have finished schooling some years ago. I wanted to prepare myself for adulthood properly, and that's what my parents wanted for me."

"Evidently if they were paying the fees demanded by Endacott, but a young person can just as easily prepare himself or herself in the world of work. You have very little experience outside of school, haven't you, Miss Stansfield?"

"Are you saying I'm not good enough for your son, Mrs Coulthurst?"

"I'm saying nothing of the kind. What I am saying is that you are inexperienced."

"Mrs Coulthurst," I reply, shaking my head in bewilderment, "David has not asked me to marry him, and unless he does I see no point in this conversation."

"Well, I can tell you, young lady, he's probably going to ask you and it's as well you're prepared when he does. I can't manage this farm much longer and I'm unsure whether David in his condition will be able to either. He isn't trained for anything other than farming and soldiering, and he's unlikely to do one and certainly can't do the other. Have you thought about that, Miss Stansfield?"

Rosie re-enters with a fresh pot of tea.

"Put it down there, girl, and go and make yourself useful in the kitchen."

"Yes, Mrs Coulthurst."

I am feeling decidedly uncomfortable. Had I known what lay in store, I should never have come here.

"I think, Miss Stansfield, you need to consider your position very carefully. I appreciate you will want time to consider it and that you need time alone. You must also talk privately with David. Beware of whirlwind romances, Miss Stansfield. One can always act in haste and repent at leisure."

I cast my mind back to Miss Buckmaster's address to the upper sixth in which she declared our marriage prospects to be so bleak. Now it seems I have been catapulted into prospective wedlock that I should reject. Why must life be a succession of absolutes such as this? I am confused, upset and even angry.

When it is time to leave David dons his overcoat and accompanies me outside.

"I don't know how to apologise," he says. "I had no idea my mother was going to be so blunt. She's a very down-to-earth woman, as one might expect from a farmer's wife, but I found her behaviour towards you totally unacceptable."

"It's all right, David – really. She must be finding life extremely difficult at present. She's lost her husband and her elder son, and now she's seen you return from France wounded. That's more than most women could bear, yet she's putting a brave face on it all – no widow's weeds, no drawn blinds, just trying to carry on as normal."

He looks pensively at me.

"She's right about one thing though. I only had to meet you once to know that you are the one for me. When you learnt I had difficulty in walking you could have made your excuses and left. I shouldn't have blamed you if you had, but you stayed and listened intently to everything I said. You fetched me something to eat and drink, whereas most girls wouldn't have even bothered to think of my needs. You're a caring person in a world where so many people don't care. It would make me the happiest man alive to be your husband, but I don't want you to answer now. You deserve and need time to think carefully on this issue. My mother is also right about that. If it will help you to make your decision, I can tell you this: I shall take on the tenancy of this farm no matter what. This wretched leg of mine should improve even though it won't mend completely. I'll get about all right. I'll have men here to do the things I no longer can. I have made my resolution. As soon as the war's over I'll get my discharge and be here permanently. Nothing and nobody will stop me."

In the two days which follow, David and I see more of each other quite deliberately so as to assist me in deciding whether he is truly the man with whom I wish to spend the rest of my life. Have I really any doubts? Frankly, I can conjure none. I talk the matter over with my parents. I thought they might have objections given that they have spent so much on my education and probably hoped a suitor could be found from the professional classes. The war, however, has changed so many of people's perceptions. Nothing is so predictable as in the past, and class barriers are becoming a little more blurred than anyone in Edwardian Britain could have envisaged.

Can I imagine myself as a farmer's wife? I had certainly not planned to become one. What would my erstwhile headmistress say? Perhaps she would advise me that it might be the only offer I am likely to get. Would it then be folly to refuse? What should become of me if I did? Were I to be an old maid, how should I earn my living? Should I be happy? Even if I could succeed as a writer, could I cope with the isolation? Would Edwin's future children come to regard me as funny old Aunt Vera, not quite like other women?

These and other questions have my mind leaping in all directions simultaneously. For sure though, if I am to accept David's proposal, then I first need to learn something about agriculture. So I elect to sample a little more of life down on the farm.

CHAPTER 5

NEW HOPE FOR THE FUTURE

Just when I need to see more of David, his home leave comes to an end and he is required to report to Aldershot. I suppose I have to remember that, despite what he calls his 'Blighty wound', he is still in the army and subject to its discipline. Our contact now, therefore, is restricted to written correspondence, there being no telephones as yet in our rural community.

We exchange letters every other day. David tells me that he is trying to 'work his ticket' by securing a medical discharge. The army, however, will have none of it and requires him to perform administrative duties. He hates being tied to a desk and has told his superiors that, if he is only fit to do paperwork, then he might as well do it for the benefit of the family farm. His commanding officer asked him whether he realised there was a war on, to which David replied that, with a chunk out of his leg, he had not got the faintest idea! This very nearly got him into hot water.

It seems that David is stuck in uniform for the duration of hostilities and there is no telling how long that will be. I advise him that I am a very busy girl, dividing my time between playing piano for wounded soldiers and trying to learn about farming from his mother and her workers. I see my parents when I return home each evening.

David is very impressed that I have graduated from feeding chickens to helping milk the cows. The dairyman, George Akehurst, is assisted by Stella, a girl from the Women's Land Army. She hails from the city and admits that she must have had a sense of humour to move from London to the wilds of Sussex. I like Stella. She is a Cockney with a never-say-die attitude to life. Her upbringing was difficult: one of seven children in a tiny overcrowded terraced house. She takes a delight in teaching me to milk because, like me, she was all at sea when she first came to the farm. Warming one's hands before pulling on the teats is apparently the secret of success.

I also help to feed the pigs. This can be quite a struggle owing to these powerful creatures being so greedy to get at the swill that they jostle me and the bucket, whereby some of its contents spill down my legs to make life wet and uncomfortable. I have been put in charge of giving the cats their milk from the dairy. They know instinctively when I am about to perform this task. One can look around the farmyard and not see a feline. Then suddenly the whole pride appear from nowhere, each one with its tail erect in expectation. They are not domesticated, so I am unable to get near enough to stroke one. If I attempt to do so, the cat will back away, seeing my friendliness as a threat.

The two shire horses, Boxer and Cedric, are wonderful. They seem to have smiles on their faces when it is time to muck them out and bring their oats, hay and water. They appear to combine gentleness with their great strength. This pair of chestnut geldings represents the bare minimum of motive power on which the farm can function. All the other draught horses were requisitioned by the army. There is, however, one more equine: Tommy, an elderly pony too light for military duties, is used to haul the trap which provides wheeled transport for Mrs Coulthurst.

Sheep graze the pastures throughout winter as their tiny feet do not poach the grass. The flock is in the tender care of a shepherd who rarely needs assistance, so I am not involved with these woolly creatures. There is just one more animal I have yet to mention. Rufus, a red cocker spaniel, is a gun dog who initially pined for his master when David's father died. The dog's feeling of loss, however, was assuaged through everyone else lavishing their attention upon him. I join in the healing process by making a fuss of him and being a walking companion. He follows his nose into every bush and hedgerow, his tail wagging in the hope of finding something interesting. What he really wants, of course, is someone to go rough shooting with him so that he can retrieve a shot rabbit

– one day, perhaps. An important fact I have to remember is that feeding Rufus is strictly the province of Mrs Coulthurst.

Thus is the livestock of Vine's Farm complete: a clucking, lowing, grunting, mewing, neighing, bleating and barking menagerie amongst whom I have made friends.

David and I have resolved to become engaged with an understanding that we shall not arrange a marriage ceremony until the war is over and we can be together. This gives us time to consider our future very carefully. My parents have advised me not to be rushed. I think this is wise counsel. David and I need to be sure we are fully committed to each other, which also involves my being committed to the farm.

In both these areas my sternest critic is Mrs Coulthurst. I sense she is watching me and, although nobody lets on, I suspect she also quizzes the labourers about my progress. She does not volunteer to show me the farm accounts. Perhaps she considers these to be none of my business while I am still, to all intents and purposes, an outsider. It is my belief David's mother cannot convince herself that an Endacott girl can adapt to the rigours of agricultural life. She probably thinks I am a middle-class adolescent playing a game, acquiring rich material with which to regale my peers at fashionable dinner parties. If so, then I am determined to prove her wrong.

One Monday afternoon in November, I am distracted from my farming labours by bells tolling at our parish church. They have remained silent since the war began. Farm staff are beginning to gather in the yard, apparently summoned by this irregular event.

"Can this be what I hope it might?" queries Stella.

I stare vacantly at her.

"You've got a bicycle," she reminds me, "and you're free to come and go as you please, so why not ride down to the station and see if anyone on a train has brought some news?"

My heart starts to race and I heed Stella's advice, grabbing my cycle and pedalling as fast as I can to the railway.

"Is it true? Is it true?" I ask the stationmaster, who performs a variety of tasks at our small country stopping place.

The fast trains from London do not call here, but the railway system provides a network of communication which reaches even wayside communities like ours.

"Yes," answers the stationmaster. "Word was brought about an hour ago. The guns fell silent at eleven o'clock this morning. I'm told crowds are thronging the capital's streets. Everybody seems to be waving a Union Jack. They've even been waving them from train windows as they pass through here."

I burst into tears and do not care if I make a fool of myself. I remount my bicycle and head back to Vine's Farm with all celerity. The eleventh hour of the eleventh day of the eleventh month, and suddenly – without expectation, it seems – this whole ghastly war is over. Can we now begin to live sensibly again?

The farmworkers discern from my demeanour and the speed with which I enter the yard that I am the bearer of important tidings.

"What news?" cries Stella, unable to wait a second longer. "Tell us! Tell us!"

I collapse into her embrace and turn to face the others with tears of relief streaming down my cheeks.

"It's over," I reveal. "We're at peace!"

There is much rejoicing, to such a degree that Mrs Coulthurst emerges from the farmhouse to enquire what all the commotion is about. Excitedly I tell her. She appears completely lacking in emotion.

"Well," she says at length, "perhaps we can all get back to work now."

It then dawns upon me that the Armistice has come too late for David's mother as it has for so many scarred by events of the last four years.

My mind now begins to focus on how soon David can be demobilised from the army. It surely has no reason to keep him any longer. Days pass and his letters give no indication as to when I can see him again. This lack of information leads me to consider other ramifications emanating from the cessation of hostilities.

On the day following the declaration of peace the parliamentary Conservative Party held a meeting at which they endorsed the coalition manifesto agreed with the Liberals during the war. There is to be a general election on 14 December – the first for eight years. It would seem the result is in little doubt. There should be a continuation of our coalition government. We learn that our Prime Minister, David Lloyd George, was dangerously ill with influenza while in Manchester during September. The news was suppressed for reasons of national morale until after the Armistice. Epidemics are no more respecters of rank than war is.

For the first time in our history women are to be permitted to vote. This is, however, only a partial concession to gender equality. Women below the age of thirty are still to be denied the franchise. How can this be fair? Younger ladies, such as Edith Nixon, if they have not been killed by the enemy, cannot vote. And is it not a scandal that conscripted men under twenty-one years cannot pass judgment in the ballot box on those politicians who sent them to war?

My small interest in politics stems from my time at Endacott. There Miss Buckmaster's advancement of the feminine cause was manifested by familiarising her charges with subjects which men thought women should know nothing about. She, like me, however, was not enamoured by the civil disobedience of Mrs Pankhurst's Women's Social and Political Union. I do not support foolish acts such as hunger striking or throwing oneself in front of a horse. Much less do I abide criminality, like breaking windows and igniting the contents of pillar boxes.

No, I would not have become a suffragette, but I would have willingly supported Mrs Garrett-Fawcett's Suffragist movement, which conducted itself in a responsible manner. I believe that it was not the militancy of suffragettes which extended the franchise, but the contribution of women to the war effort combined with political expediency in relation to ladies being obliged to vacate the workplace in favour of men returning to civilian life.

I have been wondering whether Mrs Coulthurst is entitled to vote, even though she is well past her thirtieth birthday. Women in this age group have to meet certain property qualifications. They must be a member or married to a member of the Local Government Register, a property owner or a graduate voting in a university constituency. The Local Government Register is a list of property owners who are currently paying property taxes. The problem is that David's mother is only the tenant of Vine's Farm.

Really, if she is to be denied the vote when she is over fifty, then I regard this as an absolute scandal, particularly in view of what she has suffered during the war. Tentatively I broach the subject with her. Mrs Coulthurst is not given to smiling, yet I detect an element of triumph in her countenance when she tells me in confidence that her late husband purchased one of the farm cottages as a possible retirement home. Ownership of this property is now vested with her. So she qualifies, but, I fancy, only by the skin of her teeth.

Not surprisingly Mrs Coulthurst resolves to exercise her newly won right and play her small part in deciding the composition of the next Parliament. Tommy is harnessed to the trap on polling day, and my intended mother-in-law takes the reins. I am to accompany her. My duty will be to look after Tommy while his mistress places her cross in the box of her choosing.

The local polling station is the corrugated-iron village hall. We see a few people drifting towards this unlikely centre of democracy and an even smaller number emerging from it. Of course this is a sparsely populated area and many of those eligible to vote will have to finish a day's work before they can do so. I am reminded that the last time I visited this building was when I first met David. My only companion now as I wait outside is Tommy, through whose nostrils I blow air softly from my mouth. The head carter at Vine's Farm has taught me that horses regard this gesture as an act of friendliness. I suspect, however, that Tommy might find a nosebag even friendlier.

An expression of suppressed achievement can be detected on Mrs Coulthurst's face as she hitches up her long skirt and climbs into the driver's seat of the trap. She has spent the better part of her life being denied a basic democratic right and I am glad she has lived long enough to see justice done to her.

It will be a fortnight before the election result is known. This is to give our dispersed armed services personnel a chance to vote. No rational individual should object to this. My major concern now is to have David home for Christmas. It would be just typical of the army to require him for nothing in particular during the festive season, but, joy of joys, he writes to tell me that he will be here. It provides an opportunity for my parents to meet him and his mother.

I have now learnt to drive the trap and have formed a bond with Tommy. I think he knows what to do no matter what I call to him or what instruction I communicate through the reins. This is just as well. I do not want any disasters. On Christmas Eve, I meet David off the train. He has travelled via London and is laden with presents. I have scarcely been happier. He is still noticeably lame, yet can walk a little better aided by his stick. This must have been a hindrance to him with all these parcels, but cab drivers and railway porters showed consideration to a wounded man in uniform. We return to Vine's Farm, where Mrs Coulthurst chides her son for being extravagant. He tries to convince her that this is a very special Christmas for all of us.

The next day my parents come to visit with my brother, Edwin. A large chicken with all the trimmings has been prepared for luncheon. Rosie has the day off, so I arrived earlier on my bicycle to assist Mrs Coulthurst. David has laid the dining-room table. Everything on our plates for each course has been produced on the farm. The Stansfield family are hugely impressed and congratulate David's mother, who acknowledges the compliment somewhat lugubriously.

When we have eaten, David and I volunteer to do the washing-up to give my parents time to speak privately with Mrs Coulthurst. This means that Edwin, much to his displeasure, is banished to the kitchen and handed a tea towel.

The day goes well with an exchange of gifts, including a small hamper of home-produced victuals for my parents' table. David drives my family in the trap back to our home while I follow on my bicycle. The single bench seat of the trap is just wide enough to accommodate three adults. Edwin therefore is obliged to sit on the hamper in the luggage space behind and suffers the full force of jolts dispensed by the flint road. He looks a little miffed.

Three days later, the votes in the general election are counted.

It is, as most people predicted, a victory for the coalition. It wins 523 seats, of which 382 are Conservative. The opposition appears weak, with just twenty-eight Asquithian Liberals and sixty-three Labour MPs in addition to the Irish seats. Lloyd George is to continue as Prime Minister despite being leader of the Liberal Party when the Conservatives have a substantial overall majority in the House of Commons.

New Year's Day! What will 1919 bring? David returns to Aldershot on 2 January. My parents are impressed with him – not least, I suspect, because he was wounded in action and reached the rank of captain. Momma and Poppa know there will be difficulties, but they are pleased that I shall be settled at a time when eligible men are at a premium.

Now the war is over, David and I decide to fix the date of our wedding. We choose 1 March, which is apposite because it is St David's Day! The banns are read in our parish church on three successive Sundays and there are no lawful impediments to the union. My mother delivers a private talk to prepare me as best she can with regard to conjugal rights. No matter how avant-garde Endacott's approach to female education, the curriculum has not advanced to such intimate concerns.

The main question now is whether I am to marry a soldier or a farmer. David has left the army in no doubt that he desires his release as soon as possible. It is ironic that his current administrative duties involve the processing of large numbers of military personnel back into civilian life. He and I can scarcely wait for it to be his turn.

I write to inform Dotty and Lilian of my good fortune. I hope they do not think I am being in any way immodest for as yet they have no nuptial plans of their own. I do not fear for Lilian. Her beauty and talent should ensure a plethora of suitors. It is Dotty whom I worry about. For this reason, and the fact that Lilian is so busily engaged in her London stage work, I ask Dotty to be my maid of honour, and she graciously accepts.

Lilian has replied in a most generous way, which leaves me

gasping. She is starting a new play in the West End, which also entails her singing one song. I receive two complimentary tickets for front seats in the stalls on the evening of my wedding day. If that is not enough, a room has been reserved at the Ritz Hotel for David and me on our wedding night! I respond by saying that this is too extravagant, but Lilian brushes it off by telling me she has frequented the hotel as a dinner guest on numerous occasions. This patronage, coupled with a few theatre tickets, seems to have persuaded the management to offer a little largess in return.

My father, of course, will give me away. David is having difficulty in selecting a best man. He would have chosen his brother, Vere, had the war not claimed him, with so many others. In the end he makes a splendid gesture through inviting my brother, Edwin, to fulfil the role. Edwin will only just have celebrated his thirteenth birthday, so it is something of a daunting prospect for him. He accepts despite my advising him that he will be expected to make a speech at the reception. Wisely he decides to play it safe by reading from a sheet of paper. I help him to prepare his address and then submit it for my parents' approval.

"Just don't lose the wedding ring," I warn him.

We learn that David is to be demobilised in May. Grudgingly he deems this to be reasonable since he will be home in time for haymaking. He has also acquired some leave to cover not only the wedding, but a short honeymoon too. Matters certainly seem to bode well for 1919.

CHAPTER 6

1919

The first calendar year of peace should herald a time of relief and an opportunity for reflection as well as hope. For many it does not start well because the influenza epidemic is still raging and claiming lives. Whether it is a particularly virulent strain or it just takes unfair advantage of people weakened by more than four years of war is a moot point.

Mercifully I am unaware of any contractees or deaths arising from this pestilence in our small rural community. Dotty and Lilian, too, have survived unscathed, despite living in more densely populated areas.

I have taken to reading my father's newspaper on a regular basis to familiarise myself with events in the outside world. On 20 January *The Times* reports the opening of the Conference of the Allies in Paris. The French President, Raymond Poincaré, welcomed delegates with a speech in which he identifies the task of 'laying the foundation of a new order of international peace and justice'. This sounds all well and good, but I question what it means in practice. I may be a little cynical, yet 'a new order' suggests something oppressive. It seems to me that the victors will be ordering the vanquished, and the time may come when the vanquished will not be prepared to be ordered about any longer. An aura of retribution is in the air, with people demanding reparations from Germany and even suggesting that the Kaiser should be put on trial. I can understand the anger after so much suffering, but I cannot help thinking a more conciliatory approach might be more prudent.

In February, the spectre of industrial unrest at home rears its ugly head through miners, railwaymen and transport workers resurrecting their pre-war 'triple alliance', which, had hostilities not broken out, might have led to a general strike in the autumn of 1914. Now that the common enemy of Germany and her allies has been defeated, it seems that industrial muscles will again be flexed. David tells me that girls such as I should not worry our pretty little heads with these matters. I inform him that women may no longer tolerate being kept aloof from issues which affect us all.

I do, however, have a more pressing concern. My wedding is rapidly approaching.

When the most significant day of my life arrives the weather is at least dry. David and I are married in the parish church with every pew occupied. It appears to be the highlight of the year so far for local inhabitants. Everyone is hugely excited. Dotty and young Edwin carry out their duties efficiently. Following the ceremony we are treated to a guard of honour – not the military kind usually associated with a groom married in uniform, but a rustic version of crossed pitchforks provided by the farming community.

We repair to the village hall for our reception, where lashings of locally produced food adorn the trestle tables. Edwin delivers his speech with aplomb and receives tumultuous applause for his performance. There is much merrymaking and everyone wishes us well for the future. When the time comes for David and me to leave we are given a special treat. My mother-in-law's landlord, the Earl of Cloudsley, makes his chauffeur-driven motor car available to take us to the railway station.

So we journey to London by rail and, as befits the occasion, we travel first class. Upon arrival at Victoria we hire a cab to take us to the Ritz Hotel, where it seems we are expected as though we are of special importance. We are shown to our room and presented with a bottle of champagne, compliments of the management. There is a knock at the door, and when I answer it Lilian appears, her arms outstretched to welcome me.

"Darling!" she exclaims. "I just had to breeze in and see you as

I missed the wedding. I'm so sorry I couldn't be there."

I introduce her to David.

"So you're the lucky boy, then," she bubbles, planting an impromptu kiss upon his cheek. "Ooh, look at his medals!"

"They arrived just in time for today," I tell her.

"Are they for bravery?" Lilian enquires.

"Not really," answers David modestly. "They're Pip, Squeak and Wilfred."

Lilian gives a shrill theatrical laugh.

"Isn't he funny, Vera? Go on, David – tell us what they really are."

"The 1914–15 Star, War Medal and Victory Medal," he explains. "Everybody gets the last two. The first is for those of us who volunteered before conscription came in."

"Oh, isn't he modest, darling. He must be brave to have gone to the front and he's been wounded too. You poor boy! But you will be the toast of the town tonight."

I offer Lilian a glass of champagne.

"I'd love one, darling, but I have to be on the top of my form for this evening. You wouldn't like to see me squiffy on stage, would you?"

I smile sympathetically.

"Well, look at you, Vera – Mrs David Coulthurst already. What would Miss Buckmaster say? Eight months ago she was telling us we'd probably be spinsters for the rest of our lives, and here you are belying everything she said."

"I'm very lucky, Lilian, and I know it."

"So am I," interjects David.

"I think you make a wonderful couple. Now you must come and see me in my dressing room after the play – promise?"

"Promise," I respond.

"I must fly," says Lilian. "Duty calls. Toodle-oo."

We thank her profusely for what she has done for us, but she dismisses it as nothing, making her exit like a grande dame of the theatre. David and I look at each other, trying not to laugh.

"What a girl!" he exclaims.

"Yes," I concur, "she's always had that extra dimension to her personality, but deep down she'll never disappoint you. I'll never forget her singing to those wounded soldiers back home. She had a kind of magic. She's a very special person."

Just how special Lilian can be is brought home to me that evening. Having dined at the Ritz, David and I arrive at the theatre, whereupon we are escorted not to our scheduled seats, but to a box near the stage. It is explained that we shall have it to ourselves, and there is no mistake – everything has been arranged.

Despite her tender age, Lilian gives a flawless acting performance and the highlight is the one song she has to sing to a piano accompaniment. There are five curtain calls, at the end of which the male lead, a well-known actor, steps forward to address the audience.

"Ladies and gentlemen, one of our young actresses, about whom you will all be hearing a lot more in the years to come, has an announcement to make."

Lilian approaches the edge of the stage.

"Ladies and gentlemen," she begins, "we have two very special guests here tonight. One is an old school friend of mine whom I shared a room with for two years, and the other is a brave army officer who was wounded at the front during the Great War. Today is their wedding day and I am sure you would like to give them your warmest wishes for their future happiness. I proudly present Captain and Mrs David Coulthurst!"

The grand piano in the orchestra pit strikes up Mendelssohn's Wedding March and the packed house stands to applaud and cheer us. We rise in acknowledgement and wave to the people below. I feel very nervous, even a little faint, and tears are rolling uncontrollably down my cheeks. David clasps my hand in support, and it seems for thirty seconds at least that we are the most important couple in London.

We keep our promise by visiting Lilian in her dressing room.

"That was a wonderful gesture of yours, Lilian," I confess.

"It's the magic of the theatre, darling. Weren't you thrilled by the applause?"

"Yes, but I was terribly nervous."

40

"Don't you think I am when I'm waiting to go on?"

"I don't know. You don't seem a bit nervous to me."

"That's where the acting comes in. It's all about convincing others you're somebody else with different feelings from your own."

"You're superb at it."

"Hear! hear!" echoes David.

"Oh, you're both so sweet. Now let us have a drink together in that divine hotel of yours, and then I must leave you; after all, it is your wedding night."

Yes, it is our wedding night, and Lilian does not delay us for long. She gives me a mischievous grin as she leaves the Ritz, whereupon David and I repair to our room.

I admit to being more than a little nervous and, perhaps to my surprise, find that David appears no less apprehensive. We sit for a few minutes on the edge of the bed and talk.

"I am completely inexperienced, David, but at least you know I have kept myself pure for you."

"I never doubted it," he answers gently, and goes on to confess that he is correspondingly virginal.

I admonish myself for thinking that he must have sown some wild oats given the many temptations which must have presented themselves in France, and I love him all the more for his abstinence. So we are two lovers who now discover the joy of forbearance. We belong to each other and never shall any third party come between us.

David is concerned that his war wound may impede our ecstasy in intercourse – that his discomfort may cause me distress and leave me unfulfilled. I clasp him to my bosom, kiss him and let it be known that no Teutonic piece of shrapnel, even though it has been removed, is going to compromise our devotion.

I enter the wedding bed first and lie back, not thinking of England or duty or expectation, but of my dearest and only sweetheart whom holy matrimony has joined to me. Willingly I give myself to him, and he to me. Now we are truly one. Our marriage is consummated and we shall be together until death us do part.

We have a lovely day in London before returning to Sussex in the evening. It has been the shortest of honeymoons, yet so memorable that I shall treasure it forever. Of course it has been like a fairy tale, and I must now adjust to the reality of future life. I resile from calling this a harsh reality, although I am under no illusions that being a farmer's wife is anything other than a taxing existence.

Indeed, the countryside in 1919 bears no resemblance to the comforts in parts of the metropolis. There is very little mains water, no gas or electricity; and if a motor vehicle passes, then everyone stares at it as though it has descended from another planet. The roads are laid with flint, not cobbles, and bicycle punctures are frequent, as I have known to my cost.

Water at Vine's Farm is drawn from a well situated outside the scullery. Over the stone sink inside we are blessed with a pump connected by a pipe to the well. Thus we are spared having to fetch water in pouring rain whenever the kettle needs replenishing. Cooking is done on a kitchen range fuelled by logs obtained from woodland on the farm. The range has a tank which provides us with hot water on tap. At night we rely on oil lamps or candles.

I consider it a good thing that both my parents' house and Endacott College are rurally based. They both have running water, but no modern methods of cooking or lighting, so my formative years were partly a preparation for life in my new abode.

My mother-in-law has shown no signs of moving to the retirement cottage which enfranchised her. There are perfectly good reasons for this at present. She is still the tenant of Vine's Farm and the cottage has not yet been made fit for human habitation. So married life will begin with the other Mrs Coulthurst living with David and me. Some might regard this arrangement as a recipe for disaster, not least because my mother-in-law is not the most gregarious of women. She is, however, both hardy and pragmatic.

There are still another two months to go before my husband will be free of the army for good. Military demobilisation has proved to be a most contentious issue. Following the Armistice the Ministry of Labour devised a scheme whereby personnel most needed for industry would be the first to be released. As these men tended to be the most recently conscripted, longer-serving soldiers considered this to be unfair. Mutinies occurred in camps at Folkestone and Calais while 3,000 men marched from Victoria Station to occupy Horse Guards Parade in protest.

The Secretary for War, Winston Churchill, has now scrapped the scheme and replaced it with a system of 'first in, first out'. As David enlisted in 1914 he really should be home soon for good. I suppose, because he is now an officer, the army thinks it can retain him longer to do paperwork. I do believe this is wrong, particularly as he has been wounded.

Perhaps, however, I should not be so selfish since many families have suffered from the conflict to a degree which I can scarcely contemplate.

Now, in March, there is another mutiny, this time involving Canadian soldiers encamped at Rhyl, in North Wales. It seems that a shortage of shipping is delaying the repatriation of our overseas comrades thus leading to discontent. The disturbance is put down, but tragically at the cost of some lives. Oh dear – I thought we were supposed to be at peace, and now we are killing each other!

On 3 April, I celebrate my nineteenth birthday. I can hardly believe I am still that young. So much has happened to me in less than a year that I feel I must be in my mid twenties.

In May, David is at last discharged from military service. He hangs his uniform in a wardrobe and vows never to wear it again. It is so good to have him permanently at Vine's Farm although his army pay is no longer available. Within a few days his mother confronts us both at supper one evening. Her name is Clara so I shall refer to her as such in order not to cause confusion with myself. We are, after all, both Mrs Coulthurst now.

Clara explains that farms are traditionally let by the year from old Michaelmas Day, which falls on 11 October. She makes it clear that she wants David to take over the tenancy so that she can retire. This will necessitate a visit to Lord Cloudsley's agent at the estate office.

An appointment having been made, the three of us set out to make our intentions known. We think matters might be a formality, but we are soon to be disillusioned. Mr Bodle, the agent, lugubriously reveals his employer's plans for the estate.

"As you probably know," he begins, "His Lordship's only son and heir was killed on the Somme nearly three years ago. His Lordship has two daughters, both married, who show no interest in rural activities. He has therefore decided to retain only Cloudsley Hall and the Home Farm, which he already has in hand. All the tenanted holdings he intends to sell as prices are now buoyant. I say this in the strictest confidence as letters of explanation are still to be dispatched."

David and I sit there glumly unable to speak. It is left for Clara to reply.

"So Vine's Farm is to be sold from under us," she mutters.

"There will be an opportunity for current tenants to purchase at a discount," Bodle advises.

"Chance'd be a fine thing," retorts Clara. "Where should we stand with a new landlord?"

"That would depend on him, Mrs Coulthurst. He might be prepared to let the farm to you or your son. Alternatively he may wish to take it in hand."

"Which would put us out in the cold," Clara surmises.

"That could be avoided by purchase."

"Indeed, Mr Bodle, and how much would His Lordship want for Vine's Farm, might I ask, taking into account the reduction?"

"If one includes the house, cottages and steading, Lord Cloudsley would be prepared to accept £40 an acre."

"I bet he would! There's 150 acres!"

"So £6,000, Mrs Coulthurst."

"Six thousand pounds!"

"It's very reasonable, Mrs Coulthurst, when one considers the current prosperity in agriculture."

"And how long do you think that prosperity's going to last, Mr Bodle?"

"I really couldn't say."

"No, I don't suppose you could. Only a damn fool would buy at the top of the market and see himself ruined on the altar of government policy."

"I think perhaps you should give yourself time to consider your options, Mrs Coulthurst. There's no immediate hurry, but His Lordship would like everything settled by Michaelmas."

We emerge from the estate office in silence, and this taciturn approach to our predicament continues as Tommy and the trap rattle us homeward. There is only one thing dominating our thoughts: money, or rather the lack of it.

That evening, the three of us having racked our brains for a solution, we finish our supper and have a conference around the kitchen table.

The most obvious question we have to answer is how much cash can we raise? Clara, having been left the entirety of her late husband's estate and that of her elder son, has a little over £300 in the bank as well as owning all the livestock and deadstock on the farm. David has been careful with his money while serving in the army. His gratuity and savings from his pay amount to something in excess of £200. My parents gave us £100 as a wedding present and, in the light of our having all domestic needs extant at Vine's Farm, we asked for other gifts to be in the form of cheques. These amount to about £50. I have another £50 in a post office savings account.

Clara has agreed that, in return for a roof over her head, she is prepared to sell her intended retirement cottage. It is currently in poor condition, but might raise £250. Hence we can barely muster £1,000 towards a farm priced at 6,000. I could, I suppose, ask my parents to loan us some money. They are far from poor, yet scarcely rich either. Besides, there is Edwin's future to think of. He can hardly be denied a private education to the age of eighteen when I have been so advantaged.

I seek further information from Clara and David regarding

farm profitability, rental payments and soil type. I ask them about marketing of produce and crop yields. I enquire as to the workforce and wages. My husband and mother-in-law begin to wonder why I am exhibiting all this curiosity when the only salient question seems to be one concerning lack of capital.

"And don't forget," says Clara gloomily, "we can't spend everything we've got on trying to buy this place. All businesses need working capital. Things have to be paid for before we get a return."

That night I lie in bed next to David unable to sleep. Neither of us is relaxed or content enough to make love. I am acutely aware that money seems to drive everything and that insufficient financial resources are forever dashing our hopes and aspirations.

The following morning I let it be known that I am going to visit my parents. I set out on my bicycle. When I reach the end of the lane which accesses the farm I should turn left for the village where my family reside. In a capricious moment, however, I turn right and head for the open countryside.

Within ten minutes I see the iron gates and twin pillars leading to Cloudsley Hall. I stop to gaze along the gravel drive as though mesmerised by the grandeur of this entrance compared to every other property in the district. I suppose that I should turn around and cycle back to where I came from, yet what drew me to this location?

Some inexplicable force compels me to venture forth along the drive. The gravel impedes the progress of my bicycle, so I find it easier to dismount and push my machine as I walk. Cloudsley Hall with its imposing contours causes me to pause, but dogged determination then impels me to continue until I arrive at the stone steps leading to the front entrance. Having parked my bicycle, I climb the steps and tug at the iron bell pull. The door is answered by the butler – a tall man, who stares down at me.

"Yes?"

"I, er, wonder if I may see Lord Cloudsley?"

"Do you have an appointment?"

"Er, no."

"I shall see whether His Lordship is available. Will you come in, please?"

I am led into the hall and invited to sit upon an oaken bench without cushions.

"Whom shall I say is calling, Miss?"

"Mrs Vera Coulthurst of Vine's Farm."

"I beg your pardon, madam. Please wait."

It seems that I am kept waiting for an eternity, during which time I am beset by further doubts concerning my visit. Eventually the butler returns.

"Will you come this way, madam? His Lordship is in the study."

I feel my heart racing and my mind becoming confused about what I intend to say.

"Mrs Vera Coulthurst, My Lord."

"Thank you, Sellars. You may leave us."

"Very good, My Lord."

Lord Cloudsley rises briefly from the leather chair behind his desk and signals me to be seated. He seems at pains to put me at my ease.

"Well, this is a pleasant surprise, Mrs Coulthurst. It is not every day that a young lady wishes to see me. How may I help?"

"It's about the future of Vine's Farm, My Lord."

His Lordship looks intently at me.

"Would it be more apposite to say it is about the present incumbents of Vine's Farm, rather than the farm itself?"

I try to smile, but find it difficult.

"Yes," I confess.

"Then perhaps you would take morning coffee with me. I usually partake at this hour."

"Thank you. That is very kind."

Lord Cloudsley rings a bell, which summons the butler, who is instructed to bring refreshments.

"Before I begin, My Lord, I should like to take this opportunity of thanking you in person for your wonderful gesture in making your motor car available at my wedding."

"Ah yes, I have your letter of gratitude here. You write very articulate correspondence if I may say so. Where were you educated?"

"At Endacott Ladies' College."

"Were you indeed? I sent both my daughters there."

"I'm afraid I didn't know them."

"Oh, you wouldn't have. They left more than ten years ago. You're far too young."

"I was so sorry to learn about the loss of your son, My Lord."

I can see that this reminder pains him deeply.

"Yes, my only son, three years past nearly – July the 1st 1916, the blackest day the British Army has ever known. My wife took it very badly. So many families have been similarly affected – yours too, I believe."

"A brother-in-law I shall never meet," I explain, "His name was so close to mine – Vere as opposed to Vera. You probably know my husband has a leg wound?"

"Indeed. Tell me: isn't that going to interfere with his ability to farm?"

"He will be restricted to certain tasks, yes. He certainly won't be able to walk behind a plough for hours on end, if at all."

His Lordship ponders upon this point and I sense he is wondering whether David should abandon any prospect of a farming career.

Sellars returns with a silver salver bearing coffee pot, milk, sugar and two cups and saucers accompanied by a plate of shortbread. It is the finest coffee and provides me with a welcome stimulant with which to broach the main purpose of my visit.

"I understand from your agent, Mr Bodle, that you are desirous of selling Vine's Farm, My Lord."

"Yes, with some regret I have resolved to dispose of all the tenanted holdings now that I have no one to pass the whole estate on to. So many sons and heirs of country estates like this have perished on the battlefield that I suspect there will be several such sales. The face of British agriculture is set to change with the break-up of estates into smaller holdings with more owner-occupiers. I daresay those possessed of a democratic disposition will welcome this development."

"Neither of your daughters is interested, then?"

"Good heavens, no! They both married professional gentlemen in London who had the good fortune to survive the war. All they'll ever want from this property is the money a disposal will bring. When my wife and I are gone, I expect it will all go – even this house. Some war profiteer will probably buy it! That's the sort of thing a war brings. It's an ill wind which blows nobody any good."

"As you say, My Lord, and that wind is threatening to blow our lives away at Vine's Farm."

"Don't you find the prospect of owning a property preferable to renting one?"

I feel that we are coming to the nub of the issue and I cannot skirt round the problem any longer.

"It's a question of affordability," I confess. "Mr Bodle tells us your asking price is £6,000, and we should struggle to raise 1,000."

"Given the current prosperity in agriculture, Mrs Coulthurst, that is a very fair price. I have incorporated a discount as your mother-in-law is the tenant."

"The problem is, My Lord, that prosperity will soon disappear."

Lord Cloudsley is visibly taken aback at my pronouncement.

"Indeed, young lady, are you some kind of clairvoyant? If so, then the Chancellor of the Exchequer may have need of your services!"

"With the greatest respect, My Lord, it is not a question of clairvoyance, but one of common sense."

"The only thing I can say about common sense, Mrs Coulthurst, is that it is not very common. Perhaps you would elucidate?"

I am beginning to grow in confidence.

"Before the war, going right back to the repeal of the Corn Laws in 1846, British agriculture declined and even fell into depression. The opening up of the North American prairies in the 1870s further lowered the price of corn. Refrigerated ships from the Antipodes in the 1880s lowered the price of meat. That's good news for the housewife, but rotten news for the British farmer who cannot compete because he's operating on a much smaller scale. When the war came there was a German submarine threat to our shipping. Many ships were sunk and others had to carry munitions. So food became scarcer and therefore more expensive. We had to grow greater quantities of it at home, so the British farmer has prospered. Now the war's over it won't be long before ships can concentrate on importing increasing amounts of food without danger of being sunk. Therefore food will become cheaper and British farming will go down again."

"And yet you still want to farm?"

"Yes, at the right price; it's my husband's life."

"Did you learn all this at Endacott, Mrs Coulthurst?"

"Some of it, yes; I like history. Of course I've talked matters over with my husband and mother-in-law."

His Lordship looks somewhat nonplussed.

"Another cup of coffee, Mrs Coulthurst?"

"That's very kind, thank you."

"Do help yourself to more shortbread."

"Thank you."

"Forgive me for asking, but how old are you now?"

"I'm just nineteen."

"Hmm, you're very advanced for your age, if I may say so."

"You may and I'm flattered."

Lord Cloudsley can hold his serious pose no longer. He suddenly bursts into laughter. I pretend not to understand why.

"So how much do you think I should ask for Vine's Farm, then?"

"I should say £30 per acre is plenty. It's more than we can afford without having to secure a loan from the bank."

"And why should I take £30 an acre when I can get forty or perhaps more – assuming, of course, that I am not a philanthropist?"

"I have an idea."

"You mean that, not content with expostulating an economic analysis, you now wish to advance a theory of solution?"

"Well, yes," I answer, sensing that he is surreptitiously teasing me.

"Please, Mrs Coulthurst, the floor is yours."

"I believe you wish to retain Home Farm rather than sell it."

"Yes."

"Why?"

"I already have it in hand and it provides this house with victuals."

"If you keep it, its value will decrease as farming declines. Why not sell it now with vacant possession at the highest price you can obtain? Its acreage is similar to that of Vine's."

"Then I should have no farm at all and I'll have to buy in much of our food. We could continue to produce vegetables in our walled garden and maybe run a few chickens in the grounds for eggs, but not much else. Wait a minute – are you suggesting I should sell Home Farm and keep Vine's Farm with your husband as my tenant?"

I had not thought of this, but the notion has merit.

"That would be a possible solution," I admit, "but not the one I have in mind if you are set on disposing of Vine's Farm."

"Well, I am set on it, Mrs Coulthurst."

"Then so be it at £30 an acre," I retort with an impudence of which hitherto I thought myself incapable. "If you will do this and sell Home Farm, as I suggest, then my husband and I will undertake to supply this house with dairy produce at cost during the residency of you and/or your wife."

There follows a stony silence not unlike that experienced by recalcitrant girls at Endacott when arraigned before Miss Buckmaster, the headmistress. I do hope I am not blushing with embarrassment. I feel that the longer it takes for Lord Cloudsley to reply, the more uncomfortable I shall become.

"Mrs Coulthurst, does your husband or mother-in-law know you are here today?"

"No, My Lord."

"I thought not. Well, you are a most extraordinary young lady. I have never met anyone quite like you before. I want you to return home and tell your husband and his mother what you have told me. If they are amenable to your plans, then your family may purchase Vine's Farm at £30 per acre, but you must complete the transaction by Michaelmas at the latest. Furthermore, I shall hold you to the condition that you supply this house at cost with milk, butter and cheese, and I shall require this agreement in writing."

I cannot contain my euphoria. Having thanked Lord Cloudsley profusely, I take my leave and head straight back to Vine's Farm. It is only as I near my destination that I begin to have doubts about how my success will be received.

The kitchen table serves not only its primary purpose, but also as a kind of boardroom item of furniture around which we sit to discuss serious matters that usually have money as their common denominator. Clara and David listen to my revelations with a curious combination of intrigue and shock.

"Thirty pounds an acre, you say," returns Clara without a trace of further emotion.

"That's a reduction of £10," enthuses David.

"I'm well aware of the arithmetic, son. The fact remains we should still need 4,500 for the freehold."

I point out that I am yet to ask for a loan from my parents, and, in any event, we cannot avoid a mortgage. The current rent for Vine's Farm is thirty shillings an acre per annum. If we purchase the farm, then £225 each year will be freed to help defray mortgage repayments.

In the days which follow I persuade my father to lend us £500. I am to repay him at £1 per week from money I earn by working on the farm. As an act of generosity he does not charge me interest. In the event of my parents' demise prior to repayment of the capital, my inheritance will be diminished by the outstanding sum. This will ensure that Edwin is not disadvantaged.

In the final analysis we have scraped together a deposit of £1,500 to buy Vine's Farm and borrowed the remaining 3,000 from the bank at an interest rate of five per cent per annum over twenty-five years.

The peace treaty with Germany is signed on 28 June. It is called the Treaty of Versailles and it imposes reparations upon our erstwhile enemy. These demands are not as severe as some people would like, but they are severe enough to cause much bitterness. Both David and I fear that the peace may not have been truly won and 'the war to end all wars' might prove to be an illusion.

In September, we have a rail strike and our community's major access to the outside world is shut down. This has serious repercussions for the transport of our milk to the nearest town. The journeys have to be made by road, which is slow and inconvenient.

There is a rumour that our Prime Minister, David Lloyd George, allowed the President of the Board of Trade to provoke the strike by refusing to cancel a threat to reduce railwaymen's wages. With the main arteries of our nation paralysed, Lloyd George rides to the rescue and settles matters on the strikers' terms. The true motive for this strange behaviour would seem to be a severing of the 'triple alliance' which the railwaymen had with miners and transport workers, thereby averting the possibility of a general strike. Lloyd George is perceived in some quarters as the hero of the hour through getting Britain moving again. Politics is truly a weird business.

I cannot record 1919 as a happy year for our country, although, on a personal level, I am so pleased to have married David and to have a farm we can call our own, notwithstanding a mortgage.

There is a silver lining as the year draws to a close. On 28 November a by-election is held in the seat of Plymouth Sutton. The successful candidate is Nancy Astor, standing as a Coalition Conservative. On 1 December she becomes the first woman to take her seat in the House of Commons – hurrah!

CHAPTER 7

THE ECONOMY OF SURVIVAL

As we move into a new decade I am possessed of an ambivalent disposition towards our decision to buy Vine's Farm. My apprehension is assuaged only by the fact that our wisest course – to remain as tenants, for some years at least – was taken out of our hands. It would have been a serious risk to chance that another purchaser would allow us to stay on rather than take the farm in hand. If we had been given notice to quit, then we should have lost not only our livelihood, but our home too.

So we have taken the only other option, which is a very obvious risk indeed. Whereas we can service the mortgage as matters stand, there is no doubt in any of our three minds that the fortunes of British agriculture may soon embark upon a downward slide. I find it incredible that this prognosis does not seem to be shared by the local farming community. Everyone continues to go about their business and pleasure as though nothing will ever change.

My father has lectured me concerning the responsibilities associated with borrowing money. If our farm devalues significantly, the bank may demand a cash sum to protect the level of collateral we have provided. In our particular case we have been advanced £3,000, or two-thirds of the purchase price. If the value of Vine's Farm were to fall by a half to £2,250, then the bank might ask us for one-third of this valuation – that is, £750 to preserve the security. It could be argued that our property is currently worth more than we paid for it, which gives us some leeway, but the basic principle does not disappear. If our farm devalues sufficiently, then we could be at the mercy of the bank even if we do not default on the repayments. The spectre of foreclosure is too horrible to contemplate.

Now that we have taken the plunge, the only mechanism to avoid disaster appears to be to spend as little as we can and save as much as we can. Our status may have been enhanced through becoming owner-occupiers, yet we find it necessary to budget like peasants.

The prices of both livestock and deadstock are still very high. The returns on milk are realised quickly and, following harvest, corn can be sold as soon as we wish. Sheep, however, are slow to produce a return, and we fear that a collapse in agricultural prices may precede our sale of fattened lambs or older sheep for mutton. Given the current high prices, we sell the entire flock and cease sheep farming for good. Thus we are spared the onerous task of lambing this spring. Sadly, we have had to part with our shepherd, but he has found another position on a nearby farm.

Our land girl, Stella, has expressed a wish to return to her native London, and we do not stand in her way. In one sense we are sorry to lose her, but it will be an advantage to save her wages along with those of the shepherd. As Stella will not be replaced, David and I must help our dairyman, George Akehurst, with the milking.

I take Stella with her luggage in the trap to the station. I thank her for helping to get the farm through the war and for teaching me to milk. We bid each other a tearful farewell. She waves from the carriage window as her train pulls away; and I wave back from the platform, where I remain until she is out of sight.

It is while I am delivering milk and other dairy produce to Cloudsley Hall that I have what I believe to be a brainwave. If we deliver to one house, then why should we not deliver to several houses, thereby selling at retail prices rather than just wholesale? I put this idea before Clara and David.

"Tommy and the trap aren't up to it," asserts Clara as though to scupper my plans in their infancy.

She is right, of course. Tommy is elderly and the trap too small to carry the volume of produce anticipated.

"It would take up a deal of time for one worker," adds David sceptically.

"I could do it," I retort. "If you're helping in the dairy, I shan't need to be there all day."

"What about transport, then?"

"We could buy a motor van, David."

Clara and my husband look at me askance.

"You can't drive," declares David.

"I can learn."

"A motor van costs money," Clara responds, "and we don't have much. Besides, a motor isn't so reliable as a horse."

"It's a lot quicker," I argue, "and speed is important in the countryside, where houses are thinly scattered."

This subject becomes the main talking point over the coming days. Rural folk in our locality acquire their milk by going to the nearest dairy farm with a jug or some other vessel to be filled. It is not a convenient system, particularly during inclement weather or when the farm is fairly distant. Milk deteriorates quickly unless kept cool, and this can be difficult to achieve in summer. In my opinion households would therefore benefit greatly from regular deliveries.

Both Clara and David advise me that I should investigate my market before attempting anything further. I think this is wise, not least because I am surprised that no one before has started a milk round in this area. So I tour the lanes on my bicycle, stopping frequently to enquire whether residents would support the service which I propose. I am greatly encouraged by the response, yet restrict my research to within a two-mile radius of our village.

"You'll have to go further afield if you're going to make it pay," David advises, "and that means going to the nearest town."

I did not envisage the magnitude of my task. Our small market town is some five miles distant, and I resolve to make the journey by train, putting my bicycle in the guard's van. Upon my arrival I can see immediately the wisdom of my husband's strategy. The dwellings are not only more numerous, but also densely concentrated. Of course a milk round already exists in this urban environment, it being run by a local dairy. I do not suppose it would welcome competition from a farm, but Clara is always complaining about middlemen making money at the expense of people like ourselves.

So I cycle around the residential streets, knocking on doors and asking whether the inhabitants would prefer to buy directly from a farm. I get a mixed response, although acceptances slightly outnumber refusals largely because we can supply the commodity a little cheaper.

When all my research is complete I submit to Clara and David a notebook in which I have listed names and addresses of potential customers. My efforts are well received, and, following deliberation, the ground-breaking decision is made to purchase a second-hand motor van. David learnt to drive while in the army and he will be my instructor in this exciting new activity.

The van we buy is like so many others – a Model T Ford. It was built at Manchester in 1913, but is in reasonable condition. Despite its simplicity, it is not an easy vehicle to operate. One changes gear with a foot pedal and the steering is stiff and somewhat unresponsive. The engine is started by swinging a crank situated below the brass radiator. David impresses upon me the need to wrap my thumb around the handle together with my fingers lest the crank should recoil and cause painful injury to my fattest digit.

"You'll have to remember this each time if you want to go on playing the piano." he quips.

Eventually I seem to master the art of handling this mechanical monster. The van gives a very hard ride over the flint roads and I fear that punctures may be more frequent than I should wish. David shows me how to change a wheel and satisfies himself that I can do it unaided. We have two spare wheels, each set in one of the front wings, to reduce the possibility of my being stranded by the roadside with the milk of several angry customers.

Our head carter, Jim Hobden, is not impressed with the new contraption.

"That ain't no good," he avers. "It'll break down and then it'll be nothing more than a piece o' junk. Give me a good ole 'orse any day. Like as not you'll be wanting to borrow me tumbrel to get the milk delivered afore long."

This rustic folklore of doom and gloom is most depressing, yet I dread his prediction will come true. The Model T, however, does have a reputation not only for being cheap to buy, but also for being extraordinarily robust. It is capable of going almost anywhere and is well regarded for its reliability. Armed with this knowledge, Vera, the intrepid motorist, takes to the road!

Of course our new mechanical acquisition cannot match the magnificence of Lord Cloudsley's 1912 Rolls-Royce Silver Ghost which transported my husband and I from the church on our wedding day. David tells me that it has a six-cylinder side-valve engine of more than seven litres. I do not really know what all this means except that it seems powerful, smooth and silent compared to our Tin Lizzie.

Milk rounds familiar to me generally involve a horse-drawn float carrying a large churn from which milk is ladled into receptacles provided by the housewife. We decide to modify this system through purchasing several smaller churns with handles by which I can lift them from the van to someone's house. This enables the milk to be dispensed easily at the front door – a distinct advantage during bad weather.

When we are ready to commence operations David accompanies me on our anticipated round to distribute leaflets to everyone listed in my notebook. These advise our customers that we shall begin deliveries the following Monday. We are to deliver four days per week so that household milk will never be more than two days old. I curse the fact that there are not an even number of days in the week as this necessitates delivering on both Fridays and Saturdays.

It is while we are distributing leaflets that David is able to judge my driving over a longer distance. There is no official test one has to pass, so his attestation to my proficiency is all that is required. I have noticed that, even in town, most vehicles are still horse-drawn and it is the habit of their drivers to show disdain to automobiles. There is a tendency to hold a long whip horizontally in the path of a self-propelled machine trying to overtake. When a motorist succeeds in this manoeuvre, an angry fist is often shaken in protest.

"In a few years all this nonsense will evaporate," my husband declares. "The motorised vehicle is here to stay and the horse will eventually disappear."

Monday arrives, and David wishes me well as he waves me away. 'Thank goodness for progress and mechanised transport!' I think to myself as Lizzy, as we call our van, chugs from house to house, first in the rural communities and thence to the town. I have a cashbook in which I enter all the milk purchases, and it takes the best part of a day from the time I leave the farm in the morning to the hour I return during the afternoon.

It is hard work, but I adjust myself to the routine and feel a sense of achievement. The rest days from this activity are a blessing – not that there is an absence of other duties to perform at home. I collect the money each Saturday, when I know that husbands have been paid their wages the previous day and I am least likely to be asked for credit.

Lizzy sustains her first puncture one Wednesday morning. It would have to be on my outward journey rather than the return! I am in the middle of nowhere with no other vehicle in sight. What makes this all the more irritating is the fact that it is raining. I could willingly burst into tears, but my anger precludes this possibility. I slacken slightly the nuts on the offending wheel, jack up the van and effect the necessary change. Then I let the vehicle down and check the wheel nuts are as tight as my female muscles will allow.

With a sense of triumph tempered by indignation, I load wheel, jack and wheel brace before looking in the mirror which protrudes from the offside of the van. I observe that my face is smudged with dirt – not a good advertisement when delivering milk. I wipe my cheek with a handkerchief and prepare to crank the engine. In my haste to proceed I forget what David has taught me about thumbs. Lizzy, as though to admonish me, kicks back and I pull my hand quickly away from the crank with a yelp and vocabulary which perhaps may best be described as not up to usual Endacott form. To make matters worse, Lizzy has not started. I try to calm myself and think clearly before embarking upon another attempt. Thumb wrapped round with fingers, turn smartly and let go when she fires. Hallelujah! Lizzy has started without hurting me again, so off we go.

Despite this victory sucked from the jaws of defeat, I am not in a good mood. Model Ts of this vintage are not fitted with a windscreen wiper and visibility is seriously impaired. The only concession to driving blind is to twist the upper section of the windscreen inwards so the roof protrudes beyond it, thus restricting contact with raindrops. This is a very crude attempt at improving driving conditions and not at all satisfactory.

While I am making deliveries in town, nearly an hour later than scheduled, I encounter a milk roundsman employed by the local dairy. He is a surly fellow, and he complains that I have no right to take work away from him, particularly since he fought in the war. He could not have chosen a worse day to confront me with his diatribe. Were I the relatively meek schoolgirl of two years ago I should probably have ignored him and slunk away. As it is I am in a foul temper and I let him have both barrels.

"Don't come the old soldier with me! You're not the only one who fought in the war. My husband enlisted in 1914 and was wounded. He's often in pain and walks with a stick. You haven't got a scratch!"

"You women don't know anything about war!" he counters.

The man really is making my blood boil.

"A girl from my school was killed by shellfire whilst driving an ambulance near the front. She was ferrying men like you, when wounded, to a field hospital. How dare you suggest women don't know anything about war! She's dead and you've survived intact. You don't know how lucky you are. And as for my delivering milk, it's called free competition in business. In case you've forgotten, the war was about fighting for freedom. Well, I've got just as much freedom as you and I'm going to exercise it. If you don't understand what I'm saying, I'll put it in words an oaf like you can understand: nuts to you!"

As though I have given a bravura performance on stage, a

burst of applause rings out into the street. When I look about I see housewives on doorsteps showing their appreciation. It is the other milkman who slinks away.

When I relate these events to David that evening he slaps me on the back and tenders congratulations. Even the lugubrious Clara is trying not to smile.

In 1917, motivated by Germany's newly declared policy of unrestricted attacks on shipping bound for British ports, the coalition government realised that more food would have to be grown at home. Thus the Corn Production Act came into being. This legislation has given us a guaranteed price for grain allied to a control of production costs. Agriculture has been prosperous now for three years, but at Vine's Farm we have convinced ourselves this happy situation will not last much further into peacetime.

We seem to be alone in adhering to this gloomy prospect, but now in 1920 the hammer blow finally falls. The Agriculture Act is passed, under which price controls are abandoned. I cannot see why anyone should be surprised at this since guaranteeing grain prices has proved expensive, and any government worth its salt will wish to rein in public expenditure when it is expedient. The 1920 harvest is to be the last to benefit from wartime provisions. We are not completely at the mercy of market forces, however, because the guaranteed prices are to be replaced by a cash bonus of £4 per acre for oats and £3 an acre for wheat. These concessions will nevertheless reduce our annual returns from next year.

"It looks like down corn and up horn," David remarks.

He is right, of course, and this makes our dairy herd with milk round all the more crucial to our survival. The problem is that my altercation with the urban milkman turns out to be merely a precursor to subsequent events.

The rival dairy company starts a daily delivery service, omitting only Sundays. Our customers expect us to match this. I tell Clara and David that we have no choice if we wish to continue – and continue we must. This has put enormous pressure on all of us, but we are determined to succeed.

We retain our customer base, yet our competitors play a trump card which we can scarcely be expected to copy. They let it be known that they will be abandoning the churn-and-ladle system in favour of delivering bottled milk. Of course our customers prefer this because it is perceived as being more hygienic. So the ball is once again in our court.

We respond in kind, but the stress on our resources is stretched to the limit. We have to purchase crates and numerous bottles with cardboard tops and we have only the means to bottle by hand. Clara tells Rosie, our maid, that we can only keep her on if she helps with the bottling. Like many girls of our generation she has little prospect of marriage, so employment is important to her.

She agrees readily to our proposal, and hence our maid becomes a milkmaid.

The dairy company, however, then embarks upon a price war. It reduces the cost of a pint of milk to a penny below ours. We reduce our price accordingly. This tit-for-tat nonsense continues until it is obvious that our rivals are operating at a loss. We at least produce the milk; they have to buy it in from farmers like ourselves.

I am left in no doubt about how irate our competitors are when, having delivered to one of my customers, I return to find Lizzy boxed in by two milk floats.

"Let me out, please," I ask as politely as I can.

"Why should we?" retorts one of the milkmen.

"If you don't, I'll move you myself."

My two obstructers laugh derisively.

"What do you know about horses?" one of them enquires scornfully.

"Enough to make one move his backside," I counter. "And I should remind you that you're breaking the law by causing an obstruction."

"Why don't you fetch a rozzer, then?"

I am in no mood to delay any longer. I grab the bridle of the horse in front of my van. The animal is startled and nearly throws me to the ground. The men are preparing to jeer at my indignity when the horse bolts and crates of milk are scattered in the street.

"That's your own fault," I declare. "Now you fetch a rozzer if you want to!"

It seems that this is the last straw for our rivals, who now try to make peace through buying us out: £100 was offered.

I can tell that Clara and David are thinking seriously about the proposal. I advise them not to do anything hastily. We refuse the offer, which is then increased to £125 and finally to £150.

"They wouldn't offer that unless they're really frightened by us," Clara suggests.

"Shall we accept, then?" David enquires.

"No," I respond. "We could certainly use £150, but it is a once-and-for-all payment and would see the end of an important part of our business. I have established a good relationship with our customers and our enterprise is steadily growing. I believe we can expand further by selling eggs with the milk."

"We don't have enough hens," warns Clara.

"Then we'll get some more," I say. "We'll put them in runs with wheeled houses and fold them over pasture."

"It sounds an interesting idea," concedes David. "I suppose we could start small and build up to satisfy any increase in demand."

"Exactly!" I concur.

"Beware the fox," cautions Clara.

"The hens will be shut up every night, Mother."

"It means a lot more work, son."

"Then it's all hands to the pump," I interject. "We can prevail upon the carters to help us out."

So it comes to pass that we buy a wheeled chicken house with fenced run attached and we populate it with some point of lay pullets. Each day the contraption is moved on to fresh grass, whereby the hens fertilise the ground with their droppings. They graze the pasture and are fed wheat grown on the farm. Their only other requirements are grit and water. Eggs are collected early each morning before I set out with the van.

My main concern is to protect eggs from the rough ride afforded by our flint roads. I solve the problem by laying the egg trays amongst straw in a wooden box. To date I have not had a breakage.

A neighbouring farmer has been supplying eggs to a wholesaler under contract. Big business reared its ugly head, discounting our neighbour's bills by ten per cent on the grounds that a similar proportion of eggs was being delivered broken. This was palpably untrue and the farmer's protests fell on deaf ears. In desperation he broke the contract and was threatened with legal action. He ignored these threats, which predictably came to nothing, and he has subsequently found an honest dealer with whom he is prepared to trade. As for ourselves, I feel happier that Vine's Farm is selling at least some of its produce directly to the consumer.

To offset our expenditure on the egg enterprise we sell Tommy and the trap. David informs his mother that we are now in the twentieth century and motorised transport is the way ahead. Lizzy therefore doubles as our means of getting about. Petrol cannot yet be obtained in our small rural community, so it is an advantage to be delivering produce in town. There is a garage there with a fuel pump where I can fill Lizzy's tank together with a two-gallon can for emergencies.

One Friday evening my old school friend Dotty, comes to stay for the weekend. She left the shellshock hospital and completed a secretarial course. She has now secured a job as secretary to the owner of a firm marketing machine tools. Dotty is very happy there and I am delighted for her.

When I collect her from the station with Lizzy she seems a little concerned for me.

"You look tired, Vera."

"Oh dear – do I?"

I have scarcely had time to contemplate how hard everyone at Vine's Farm has been working. Dotty is somewhat astonished that I have learnt to drive. I tell her that it is a necessity if we are to survive.

"Just don't overdo it," she advises.

That night whilst preparing for bed I look in the mirror and see a more careworn figure than I believed myself to be.

CHAPTER 8

THE FINANCIAL NET TIGHTENS

Dotty informs me that there is a notice on the wall of her workplace in London. It reads, 'Cease using the typewriter if someone is speaking on the telephone. This is a little point which it is important to observe.' Typewriters and telephones – my goodness, how primitive we are in the countryside by comparison! I do not know of anyone who has a typewriter or telephone in our locality. There is no gas or electricity. Our village received its water main in 1905, but no water has yet been piped to the outlying properties.

Modern conveniences which many in the metropolis take for granted are conspicuous by their absence at Vine's Farm, where we are living as we might have done decades ago. The only concession to the twentieth century seems to be our motor van, which many locals view with suspicion.

In 1921, however, an opportunity arises unexpectedly. Lord Cloudsley, no doubt considerably richer through selling his estate farms at high prices, decides to have mains water laid on from the village to Cloudsley Hall. The pipeline will run parallel to the road by which our farm is accessed. We can therefore tap into this pipe and dispense with the need to draw water from our well. The chance is too good to miss, notwithstanding an associated cost to ourselves.

How wonderful it will be to have a fresh-water supply to both house and farm! Of course we shall have to pay a water rate, and we do not welcome any additional expense, but the advantages outweigh anything else.

Thus it comes to fruition that a tap appears over the scullery sink and there is another one we can use to hose down the cowshed after milking.

This initiative proves to be more beneficial than I could have imagined.

In April, I discover that I am two months pregnant. David is ecstatic. He does not admit it, but I suspect he is hoping for a boy to inherit the farm in due course. I am therefore wishing secretly for a son, although if we have a daughter I shall be no less delighted. Either way, I am so relieved my child will be born into a home with the cleanest water one can provide.

I write to tell Lilian and Dotty my good news. I do hope they are not envious as they are still unmarried.

Of course I should know better than to think they might be so disposed. Indeed, they are both fulsome in their congratulations for my confinement. Dotty is busy knitting baby clothes and Lilian, fully committed to her career, has purchased a perambulator. It arrives one day at the station for me to collect in the van.

Inevitably my pregnancy brings problems as well as joy. The time will come when I shall have to stop delivering eggs and milk. The business is doing well and somebody will have to take my place. David is willing, but the job entails much walking in addition to driving. His wounded leg is just not up to it on a regular basis. No one else on the farm can drive. Our three carters are well past fifty and show no inclination to learn new transport skills.

There is only one thing to do. We must take on a driver at a time when we are looking to control expenditure rather than increase it. The pre-war wage of an agricultural labourer was twelve shillings per week. Now, in 1921, this figure has risen to forty-six shillings, and in so doing has surpassed the rise in price of farm produce for the first time in history.

Despite all this worry we find a young man who, like David, learnt to drive in the army and fought in the trenches. His name is Bill. He and my husband have been overheard talking about the war, but neither of them will discuss it with anyone else on the farm.

I accompany Bill on the milk round for a few weeks until I am satisfied he knows all the customers and our requirements of him. He is of a pleasant disposition, despite his wartime experiences – or perhaps because of them. He is in a peaceful situation now and his sturdy frame seems to deter any urban milkman from complaining about competition.

The 1920 Agriculture Act was something of a hammer blow to arable farming, but we face even greater difficulty in 1921. Spring may have heralded the welcome news of my pregnancy, but it also coincides with a fall in cereal prices as cheap imports begin to take effect.

No sooner are our bonuses for wheat and oats paid for the 1921 harvest than the 1920 Act is repealed, thereby exposing all arable crops to the mercy of market forces. What is particularly infuriating about this latest legislation is that the 1920 Act included a clause stating that four years' notice would be given if Parliament intended to abolish its provisions. Had this clause been honoured, farmers would at least have been able to prepare in advance. As it is we feel completely betrayed. The repeal comes into effect on 1 October, which means next year's harvest and subsequent ones indefinitely will be unprotected against further price falls. Thank goodness we have established our milk round!

The 1920 Act also set up wage committees to fix minimum pay for agricultural workers. These are now abandoned; and as farm incomes dwindle, so too must wages. The lot of a labourer is not a happy one and I could weep at the prospect of telling our men they must suffer a cut in pay. This distasteful duty will fall to David when it becomes necessary.

On 7 November I give birth to a healthy boy weighing seven and a half pounds. The village midwife fusses over me like a mother hen and the doctor looks in regularly. So my son is born at Vine's Farm with his parents hoping he will spend his life here. My mother-in-law, Clara, is delighted to have become a grandparent. If I am to resume work on the farm in any capacity, I know she will be the ideal person to attend to the needs of our new arrival in my absence.

There remains the question of naming our offspring. I want to include Vere, in memory of David's lost brother, but Clara concedes this name is going out of fashion somewhat. We settle therefore on Vere as my baby's middle name, and David suggests we call him James after my late father-in-law. This is a name which has endured over the centuries, so we all agree on James Vere Coulthurst; and he seems in full agreement as he gurgles in his pram.

At Christmas both Dotty and Lilian come to stay with us. I did not think Lilian would be able to spare the time as the pantomime season is here. She tells me that she is resting prior to making her film debut in the new year. Just think – I shall be able to see her moving on screen even though she may be many miles away. Lilian has already made her first gramophone record and she presents a copy to me as a Yuletide gift. We wind up Clara's gramophone, place my present on the turntable and apply the needle to the now rotating disc. The song is called 'Whispering'. An instrumental version by Paul Whiteman and his orchestra has sold over one million copies in the United States.

We are delighted with Lilian's recording and look to see James Vere's happy reaction to the music.

"He likes it," cries Dotty.

"Out of the mouths of babes and sucklings . . ." declares Lilian. "So I must have done something right."

"You do much that is right," I tell her.

"I know," suggests Dotty: "we've heard the record – how about a live performance?"

"Yes, go on," David urges.

"I haven't got any musicians with me," protests Lilian.

"You're forgetting Vera aren't you?" Clara replies, "She plays our old piano much better than I can."

"Oh, of course," confesses Lilian. "Darling Vera, how remiss of me! You play very well."

"But I need sheet music for it," I advise, "and I haven't got any."

We are about to become disappointed when Lilian remembers having some in her suitcase which she intended to give me with the record.

"Go and get it," demands Dotty excitedly. "It will be just like that time you both entertained those poor wounded soldiers. Do you recall?"

How can we forget, although it seems almost a lifetime away now! Lilian fetches the sheet music and I sit down at the upright piano situated in one corner of the parlour. Lilian's crystal-clear voice fills the room – and to think that people pay good money to hear her in the company of hundreds! We are so privileged to know her and to have her as a guest in our home. When the performance is over, little James Vere is wriggling with excitement and showing his elation as only a baby can. It is a very happy Christmas at Vine's Farm, and I can but hope the coming year will augur well for us.

Such hopes, of course, are held on very shaky ground. In July 1921 the price of wheat was eighty-four shillings and seven-pence per quarter. Now, one year later, this figure has crashed to forty-four shillings and seven pence! During the course of 1921 the average weekly wage for agricultural workers fell from forty-six to thirty-six shillings and it is still falling. As if all this misery is not enough, the summer of 1922 is proving to be wet – a curse to those of us with a corn harvest. There is little more dispiriting than seeing sheaves of cereals stooked up to dry in the sun when all the weather can do is to soak them with rain.

Mercifully, ours is a mixed farm. At 150 acres it is too small to specialise in arable crops. Corn farmers with much capital invested in large acreages must be seriously worried. Many of those who have purchased with outstanding mortgages are in desperate straits. Only now does it appear to be dawning on our industry as a whole that we are on the cusp of an agricultural depression which could last for many years.

The repeal of the 1920 Agriculture Act was one of several measures to cut public expenditure fuelled by collapse of the post-war economic boom. I have to admit therefore that farming is not the only victim. My father continues to supply me with his *Times* newspaper when he has finished with it. There is much press reference to the 'Geddes axe'. Back in February this year Sir Eric Geddes' committee on government spending reported its findings. The subsequent 'axe' has swung violently in several directions against our armed forces, public health and education, to name but three. An earlier economy was inflicted upon the railway companies, which are to be regrouped under an Act of Parliament. Our local London, Brighton and South Coast Railway will soon be no more. It is to merge with two other companies to form the Southern Railway, and its umber livery is to be repainted green.

David tells me that economic failure undermines the credibility of government, which I suppose is an obvious truth. There are rumblings about Conservative dissatisfaction within the coalition administration. So will the coalition be destroyed from within rather than from without?

On 19 October a meeting of Conservative MPs is held at the Carlton Club. They vote to reject their leaders and continuance of the coalition with the Liberals. Austen Chamberlain resigns as Conservative leader and Lloyd George retires as prime minister. Both these positions are assumed by Andrew Bonar Law, who retired as Conservative leader last year owing to illness. He immediately dissolves Parliament. A general election is held on 15 November and we now have a Conservative government.

What is particularly worrying at Vine's Farm this year is that the milk price has also slumped. We have set great store by this commodity as the saviour of our enterprise. Despite retailing a considerable proportion of our milk, we have had to lower our price in order to remain competitive. No matter what produce we sell – retail or wholesale – our annual income has nosedived. If we had paid Lord Cloudsley the £40 per acre he was originally asking for the farm, then we should now be in serious trouble. Even at the bargain price of £30 an acre, life is a struggle. The only door left open to us seems to be to mirror government policy by reducing our expenditure.

David has suggested increasing our production. I think there might be scope for this with regard to our dairy herd, although the margin would not be significant. I cannot countenance, however, trying to grow more corn, particularly as this is such a small farm. Our cash crops are becoming crops without the cash. The problem is that our soil is not good. It is heavy weald clay and will not yield like the loams and silts in other parts of the country. A successful cereal crop, weather-permitting, can only be obtained through the principle of rotation. We have operated a four-year system of wheat followed by oats then a red clover ley followed by kale. We have also applied all our farmyard manure to the arable fields to increase the humus content.

Both Clara and David come to the conclusion that, rather than try to grow more of something which realises little or no profit, we should produce less of it or even none at all. We settle on growing only what we need to consume on the farm. The horses require oats, so we shall sow enough to feed them. The straw will be needed for bedding, and oat straw also has a low feeding value which may be of use to our fattening cattle. Thus we shall maintain a policy of self-sufficiency and only buy in those items which the farm cannot produce.

Our rotation will be simplified through scrapping wheat and allowing the clover to last for two years. We shall keep enough wheat in store to feed our hens, and only grow a little more to avoid its running out. This change will reduce the workload and hence costs as we will have to till each arable field only three out of every four years. We cut expenditure further therefore through letting one of our two under-carters go.

With these savings we elect to increase the dairy herd gradually. We take the view that prices will decrease year on year for the foreseeable future, so there is no incentive to purchase everything at once. It is scarcely an option anyway since our cash flow would not permit it without incurring further debt. In the autumn of 1920 a horse might have cost £100 and a cow £60. Now, two years on, these figures have already slumped by nearly a third.

CHAPTER 9

LEAN AND MEAN

1923 dawns and Britain does not seem to be in rude economic health. Unemployment remains a problem. The jobless total passed two million in June 1921 and, although it has fallen, there are still well over one million people without work.

Our financial situation at Vine's Farm requires constant monitoring. To cut costs and pay bills we need to boost efficiency. Only milk production, it seems, can bring a reasonable profit. Although the price of this commodity has slumped, it has not fallen so badly as is the case with corn. We must therefore continue to concentrate on dairying and try to expand our enterprise at the expense of other sectors.

There is scarcely any profit in pigs, so we raise capital through selling ours and releasing labour for the cows. David's war wound precludes him from walking with horses on the land. His solution to this handicap is to sell our two shires and replace them with a tractor. Clara, her outlook rooted in the nineteenth century, seems to think that he has taken leave of his senses. David's argument is that we can then dispense with our remaining under-carter and raise more money on the horses by selling them before their value falls any further.

"No one else round here has a tractor," argues Clara. "Even Lord Cloudsley never had one before he sold Home Farm."

"It's the future, Mother."

"The only future a tractor would bring is ruin, boy. Don't you know they cost serious money?"

"One has to speculate to accumulate," protests David.

"There's been speculation enough here already, what with a

motor van, milk bottles, folded poultry and the like."

"They are making a profit," I counter. "Even the eggs show a small return."

"Maybe, but how could a tractor make us money when corn keeps going down? We've already given up wheat, so what would be the point in growing oats if we've got no horses?"

"We need the straw," David interjects.

"All right, we need the straw. So what would you do with the grain? You couldn't sell it to our neighbours for their horses – they've got their own oats."

"We could grow barley instead, Mother."

"Oh, barley now, is it? So do you intend to encourage drunkenness amongst the population by trying for a malting sample?"

"Beer in moderation does not lead to drunkenness," I advise, reminding myself that Clara is a faithful daughter of the Church.

"What if you don't get a malting sample?" she enquires.

"I think we should use the barley for feeding our fattening cattle," explains David. "That way the beasts will fatten quicker and help our cash flow. Of course we'd need a rolling machine. This could be driven by the tractor using a belt."

Clara throws up her hands in despair.

"Good grief, boy – now it's a rolling machine too! Have you money to burn? It won't stop there, will it? You'll have to get the blacksmith to convert our wagons and implements for hauling by tractor. You won't be able to convert the plough; you'll have to buy a special one for that. Don't you see? Once you start there'll be no end to the expense, and for what? To produce arable crops that cannot be sold for decent cash, only fed to beef cattle? Horses are good enough for what we want at present."

I have to confess, albeit sadly, that Clara is right. We just do not have the financial resources to undertake a conversion to automotive power. I say 'sadly' because I know what is at the root of this argument. Before David volunteered for the army in 1914 he worked the land with horses, often from dawn to dusk. The arable side of farming was and still is in his blood.

He is now reduced to milking cows by hand under the supervision of his own dairyman, feeding these animals, mucking them out and helping Rosie to bottle milk. He feels emasculated knowing that his poor, wounded leg will not stand the strain of walking the furrows. The advent of the tractor is his potential escape route, but our financial position precludes his liberty – a liberty for which he has fought and apparently lost. I can only console and support him, trying to give him hope that one day he will be free to return to the fields.

As for my own contribution to the farm, I am beginning to assume the role of general factotum following my confinement. I help David in the dairy to be near him and I feel honour-bound to assist Clara with domestic duties now that Rosie is committed to farmwork.

Of course my responsibilities as a mother must be discharged. I take James Vere for outings in the beautiful pram which Lilian so generously gave us. It is on these little excursions that I talk copiously to my baby. Sometimes we pass the field where the soldiers' convalescent camp was situated. It has been dismantled now and no trace of the land's erstwhile function remains. Where I played the piano and Lilian sang to those dear, broken men sheep now graze. Despite this pastoral scene, I still hear Lilian's wonderful voice giving grace to 'Roses of Picardy'.

I begin to sing this song – the only sound perceivable in this tranquil setting. My voice cannot compare with the clarity and control of Lilian's, but I am reasonably competent, having sung in the Endacott choir with, yes, Lilian. I see James Vere's little face smiling up at me. He is my audience, my lovely son, and one day, when he is a farmer, tractors may be the norm and not the exception.

In May 1923, our Prime Minister, Mr Bonar Law, is diagnosed with terminal throat cancer. He resigns immediately and is replaced by Stanley Baldwin, who has the distinction of being Rudyard Kipling's first cousin. Kipling, who won the 1907 Nobel Prize for Literature, lives here in East Sussex. I still like to keep up with the news through my father's discarded copies of *The Times*. I may be somewhat isolated geographically, but I do not wish my mind to narrow.

James Vere has now outgrown his pram. He crawls about the house and will soon be walking unaided. He can say 'Momma' and 'Poppa' and has just graduated to 'Nanna', which gratifies Clara no end. I really need a pushchair to transport my son around – more expense, of course, but fortunately one we can afford.

We are about to make the necessary purchase, but Dotty intervenes. She almost demands that she provides the article herself. I do not wish to sound cynical, but Dotty loves to visit us and eat the freshest food our farm and garden can provide. Perhaps I should not reveal that Dotty is very fond of eating generally. So she invites herself and arrives at our local station armed with a folding pushchair, which is gratefully received.

In June, the weather allows us to go haymaking. The best hay is always made at this time, when most of the grasses are beginning to flower. So we go for quality rather than quantity. Mowing a meadow is one job which David can do with horses, and he insists on doing it. The mower has a seat for the operator, and the machine's oscillating knife is driven by the land wheels as the horses move forward. David informs me how important it is, when doing anything to the knife, to ensure the mower is out of gear. Failure to remember this fact can result in serious damage to one's fingers if the horses move slightly. So round the field goes my husband, performing a task redolent of a Roman charioteer orbiting an arena. He is happy now, and I only wish that he could be happy throughout the farming year.

A day or two after haymaking, provided there is no rain, it is time to turn the mown grass so its underside can be exposed to the sun. We have a swathe-turner for this job, the implement being hauled by just one horse.

When another day or two have passed, the farmer can assess whether the crop is dry enough to put into a rick. My husband makes this decision himself. While I hold James Vere in my arms, I watch as David grabs a small quantity of hay in both hands and twists it into a rope. The rope breaks easily through this action, and so he declares the crop fit to pick up. Our horse rake puts the swathes of hay into rows sufficiently wide for a wagon to pass between them. Once this task is completed our head carter and under-carter load the crop into the wagon using pitchforks. David, being David, however, assists them until his injured leg is too painful for him to continue. When Bill has finished his milk round he lends a hand, but in truth we need more workers at this busy time.

Clara tells me that haymaking before the war was a far more labour-intensive activity. The hay used to be raked by hand into windrows for drying with every available person involved, including women and children. It was something of a social occasion, with beer and lemonade being brought out to slake everyone's thirst. Shortage of labour during hostilities prompted David's late father to purchase the swathe-turner and horse rake. He also bought an elevator, powered by an oil engine, and we use it to raise hay from a wagon to the rick in which the crop is stored for winter. Without these labour-saving devices I do not know how we should manage. It is a blessing they were acquired when farming was profitable, because circumstances preclude such an investment now.

David's upper-body strength is considerable. His problem is that he suffers pain whenever he has to walk far or stand for long periods. I know that further automation would be such an advantage, yet our lack of capital renders him no relief and limits his contribution to our enterprise.

I resolve to expedite matters through returning to milk-round duties, thereby releasing Bill to work full-time on the haymaking until this task is finished. James Vere is left in the charge of Clara while I re-establish my relationship with our van, Lizzy. My customers want to know all about my baby, and they keep me talking on the doorstep for longer than I should wish. Both David and Bill wonder why I am taking so long to deliver the milk, and James Vere vents his displeasure at my protracted absence.

Our dairyman, George Akehurst, is now under greater pressure as David tries gamely to assist with haymaking and I am driving the van. Rosie has learnt to milk cows, but even she gets diverted from the cowshed during early mornings to help David and me to bottle milk before I set out on the road. We are lean, we are mean, but we are short-staffed and arguably inefficient.

I wonder how long we can go on like this, yet the hay crop is gathered in at last and there is time to take stock before our corn harvest gets under way. We really need to expand our dairy herd to produce more milk, but this would mean taking on another worker to help George when we cut the oats and what will be our last crop of wheat for some years to come.

In the event, we do nothing to avoid further financial commitments. I suppose this is a fudge, yet we muddled through haymaking, so we should be able to muddle through harvest. During August wheat turns golden brown while oats become ash blond. When these crops are ready to be cut it is then that we have an annual problem. David's father bought a self-binder during the war, but it needs three horses to pull it and we have only two. Fortunately, we have an arrangement with a neighbouring farm to borrow an extra horse at harvest time. We reciprocate by lending the binder once our corn is cut. Neither David nor I are happy about being reliant on someone else, but we cannot resolve the difficulty without spending a considerable sum on an animal which would be surplus to requirements for most of the year.

The binder cuts the corn and ejects sheaves on to the ground. These sheaves must be stooked by hand in clumps of up to ten. Each sheaf is held together by a single piece of binder twine. The stooks allow any rain to run off the sheaves, and wind can then dry them out. Corn should never be ricked immediately after cutting because it would become hot and spoil. Wheat needs nearly a week in stook during fine weather and oats a fortnight. It is in these periods that the grain hardens, thereby completing the ripening process.

Our winter-sown oats are cut first, followed by winter-sown wheat. David informs me that he can tell when oats are fit to cut by the grains being exposed in their awns. He tests the readiness of wheat by rubbing out an ear and squeezing the grains between finger and thumb. When the inside of each grain emerges like cream cheese, the crop is ready for the binder.

Binding may only start once the sun has burnt off dew from standing corn and must finish when new dew begins to form at eventide. Dry sheaves which have been stooked for the requisite period are loaded on to a wagon and taken to a place near the steading where a rick is built, the top being thatched with straw to give protection from the weather. There the crop will remain until threshing time. All seems to go well enough for our 1923 harvest, although corn prices continue to fall.

It is considered better not to sow one's own seed for next year's crop. Rather one should buy seed from another farm or a corn merchant. This is expensive unless the purchase can be offset through selling some seed corn from one's own harvest. David, following his late father's example, does precisely this. Thus it is necessary to thresh some corn during October. This is a contract job owing to the cost of the machinery involved.

One day a threshing box hauled by a traction engine arrives in our yard and the dusty, noisy business of threshing begins. Sheaves from a rick are fed into the thresher, which separates grain, chaff and straw. The machine is driven by a belt connected to a flywheel on the steam-powered engine.

I take James Vere to view this fascinating spectacle. He seems extremely interested, pointing his finger towards the activity and grinning in contentment. Grain and chaff are put into different sacks while the straw is made into a stack. Threshing is a very labour-intensive operation and anyone not otherwise engaged is busily involved with it.

On 25 October our Prime Minister, Stanley Baldwin, addresses the Conservative Party's annual conference at Plymouth. As I read my father's discarded *Times* newspaper of a few days later I am staggered to learn that Mr Baldwin has declared a policy of protectionism. I was brought up to believe that imposing tariffs on imported goods is deleterious to the interests of a manufacturing nation such as ours. We seem to have little mineral wealth except coal, and no factory owner wants to pay extra for his imported raw materials. Moreover, any tariff reform is only likely to provoke retaliation from abroad, which will render our own products less competitive.

A policy of free trade through most of the last century has made

Britain an economic success. Does Mr Baldwin not recognise this? I think he has allowed a temporary slump in our fortunes to cloud his judgment. If he needs a lesson from history, then reference to the protectionism advocated by Joseph Chamberlain nearly twenty years ago should remind him of the consequences. Arthur Balfour's Conservative government was annihilated at the 1906 general election.

It is clear that Mr Baldwin's change of policy is going to necessitate the seeking of a new mandate through another general election. We learn that one is to be held on 6 December. Clara, David and I talk about the probable outcome over the supper table each evening. David has long since refrained from telling me not to worry my pretty little head about politics. He appears convinced that enfranchisement of women has turned all feminine minds upside down and that we are now making up for lost opportunities through centuries past.

With Liberals somewhat in decline and Conservatives about to commit suicide there remains the spectre of our first Labour government. There are those who think this might precipitate a red revolution comparable to that experienced in Russia. If that is true, then as landowners we can expect little mercy at the hands of the socialist hordes. I have no doubt this is a wild exaggeration, yet I lack confidence that trade-union-backed politicians can work some economic miracle from which we may all prosper.

When the votes are counted, no one has an overall majority. Conservatives form the largest party with 258 seats. Labour has 191 and Liberals 158. On this basis Mr Baldwin continues in office leading a minority government. On 21 January 1924, however, he suffers defeat in a vote against the King's speech. The Labour Party then form a minority government of their own with Ramsay MacDonald as Prime Minister. What will this all mean?

CHAPTER 10

LEANER AND MEANER

James Vere is now more than two years old and, to my delight, he is learning to speak. My maternal instinct tells me it is so important to talk to one's child no matter how young he or she is. Whenever I am alone with my son I become an inveterate chatterbox and he has always responded, firstly through intent listening, followed by infant burblings maturing to distinct sounds and finally words. Truly nature is a wonderful phenomenon, but it needs a helping hand and I must perform a mother's duty. Perhaps I shall know my task is almost complete when James Vere is old enough to ask me to stop nagging him!

In February 1924, I learn that my experiences with James will have to be repeated for I am pregnant again. My second child is due in September. I suspect that David will hope for another boy with thoughts about the future of the farm, yet I should not in the least mind a girl now that James will ensure the Coulthurst name survives another generation.

I wish my joy in this regard could be shared with a sanguine hope for the future of British agriculture. Sadly the prices of all farm produce continue to decline and only milk production offers any residual confidence. Clearly our decision to concentrate on this aspect of our business has proved to be the right course and we have increased production through buying a few more cows either in calf or with calves at foot. Most of our milk is still put into churns and taken to the railway station, but we have steadily acquired more customers for our retail delivery service – so much so that it has become expedient to purchase a second motor van.

Such an expense has only been possible through a legacy from my Aunt Beatrice. She was my father's maiden elder sister, and in her will I received £350. My brother, Edwin, was left a similar sum, which becomes available to him when he attains his majority. I have no wish to be disrespectful to my late aunt, but I cannot help thinking hers was a timely demise.

The second van will soon present a problem, however, because we shall need someone to drive it once my confinement obliges me to rest. This latest vehicle is another Model T Ford, but a younger version than our faithful Lizzy. It is only two years old and has certain refinements, such as a windscreen wiper and windows on the doors. It is therefore a more convenient machine to operate during inclement weather, so I have bagged it for myself while Bill braves the draughts as he drives the older van.

For some weeks now, as I approach our nearby market town to deliver milk and eggs, I stare at the array of machinery displayed outside the premises of a firm of agricultural engineers. I stare on the outward journey and I stare on the way back. The reason I stare so intently is because there is one object there so alien to every farm I know in the district. Quite simply, it is a tractor. Every time I pass I expect it to have disappeared, but it stubbornly remains always in the same position.

One day, my deliveries having been completed, curiosity gets the better of me. I stop the van and go to inspect this intruder into the world of horse-drawn implements which have served the land for centuries. From the name above its radiator I can tell that it is a Fordson. It has iron wheels with spade lugs at the rear. There is also a pulley for belt-driving something – for example, a threshing machine.

No one comes to ask me whether I am interested in anything, so I walk over to the nearest building and attract the attention of a man seated at a desk and wearing a three-piece suit.

"Yes, madam?"

"I'd like to know more about that tractor you have out there."

The man looks dumbfounded.

"Is your husband with you?"

"No."

"Well, surely you'll need him to be here. We're agricultural engineers."

"That is why I have come."

"But won't it be your husband who'll be needing a tractor?"

"Yes."

"And presumably he'll be paying for it?"

The man is beginning to irritate me with his preconceived ideas about the role of women in society.

"If the tractor suits our requirements and if it is affordable, then I shall be paying for it," I tell him in a tone which leaves him in no doubt that I mean business and am in no mood to bandy words with him.

Wearily he rises from his chair and dons a bowler hat. Then we repair outside to discuss the object of my potential desire. He extols the virtues of the machine with the usual exaggeration, whereupon I invite him to start it. The act of cranking its engine while attired in a suit and bowler brings an indignity for which he is ill-prepared. The machine is started by allowing it to fire on petrol before switching the fuel supply to tractor vaporising oil – or TVO, as it is called. This gives off a rich aroma, to which I take an unexpected liking. I ask the salesman to engage and then disengage the belt pulley. I follow this with a demand that he drive the tractor a few yards forwards and backwards. This he is reluctant to do because the spade lugs on the rear wheels will scuff up his cinder-laid yard. He nevertheless relents and I nod my approval. There now remains the question of price. I am told the tractor will cost me £125.

"I need a trailed plough to go with it," I advise.

My bowler-hatted guide, still looking unconvinced that I am a serious potential purchaser, leads me to a small array of ploughs, most of which are designed for hitching to a pair of horses.

"This is the best we have," he declares. "It has the advantage of two mouldboards and shares."

"You mean it is a two-furrow plough?"

"Yes, you can do the work in half the time."

"And pull it much faster with a tractor?"

"Oh yes, madam. A single-furrow plough behind horses will

only cover about an acre a day. Your ploughing will be done in no time with tackle like this."

The plough is priced at £30. I tell the salesman it is expensive. He explains that one is paying not merely for the implement, but also for what it does. I tell him it is still expensive. He replies that such a tool will save me money. I inform him that crop prices are declining sharply and one can scarcely save anything. He coughs. I let it be known that many farmers will grass their farms down and that arable equipment will become almost worthless and therefore he will be stuck with this plough unless he lets me have it for £20. He goes red in the face and tells me I can have it for twenty-five. I demur and request that we take another look at the tractor.

"What sort of guarantee are you offering?" I enquire.

"Guarantee?" he queries. "Madam, it's second-hand."

"Are you saying it's not been well cared for?"

"Certainly not; it's in fine condition, as you can see, and only a year old."

"Well, if it's as marvellous as you profess, you can have little fear in guaranteeing it. Shall we say parts and labour over six months?"

I can almost swear the man is about to explode, the buttons on his waistcoat straining their cotton to the limit.

"It's not Christmas, don't you know," he responds sardonically. "I don't suppose there's anything else you'd like while we're about it?"

"Well, yes, there is, as a matter of a fact. I'd like you to change the engine oil, fit new sparking plugs and lubricate all the grease points; oh, and supply a spare fan belt just in case."

"And for that you'd pay us £125 plus £25 for the plough?"

"No, I'd pay £140 for the lot with a promise you'll deliver it all on May the 12th – my husband's birthday. It's to be a surprise. The guarantee is to run from that date."

My rival in negotiation is utterly perplexed.

"Are you sure you wouldn't like the petrol and TVO tanks filled too?"

"That's a splendid idea," I enthuse, "and all in with my price!"

"Can you pay now?" he asks in a mood of resignation.

"Absolutely," I reply as I produce my chequebook with a flourish.

This cheers him a little and we shake hands on the deal.

As I drive home I find myself singing one of Lilian's songs. It has not escaped my attention that the guarantee will cover the busiest period during which the tractor will be in operation. If there are to be any problems, then they should manifest themselves at haymaking, harvest or sowing time.

I have concocted a cunning plan for David's birthday. He is to accompany me on my milk round. When I have made my last delivery in town we are to lunch at an old coaching inn at my expense. This is to be his birthday present – or so he thinks. While we are away, tractor and plough are to be delivered, placed in an outbuilding and hidden under a tarpaulin.

Cometh the day, cometh the luncheon, which we enjoy and for which David thanks me sincerely.

"I'm not sure a gentleman should let a lady pay a bill like that," he quips as we emerge into the street.

"Well, it is a special day for you, darling."

"Yes, and I'm another year older; I'm thirty now. It won't be so long before I'm forty and middle-aged!"

We journey home in good spirits and I park the van in its usual resting place.

"What's under there?" David enquires, having spotted an unfamiliar hump in the barn.

I try to appear unconcerned.

"Oh well, I suppose there's only one way to find out," I reply as I saunter up to the tarpaulin and pull it clear.

"Happy birthday!"

There is a stunned silence. David is motionless. I look at his face and realise suddenly that tears are rolling down his cheeks. I have never seen him like this before. Very soon he is weeping copiously and buries his head in my chest. His whole body is shaking, which compels me to wrap my arms around him to hold him closely.

It is now that I realise for the first time what war has done to my husband. It has damaged not only his body, but also his mind, in which he has bottled up horrific images that he can share with no one save those, like Bill, who have experienced them. In marked contrast, at this moment he sees himself as the recipient of kindness unparalleled – kindness which will help him to combat those physical restrictions that have frustrated him most. Only now, through this Fordson tractor, can he take his place in the fields of Vine's Farm and feel himself a full man again.

"I'm sorry," he says at length. "I don't mean to make such a fool of myself."

I am beginning to cry a little too.

"We make a right pair, don't we?" adds David. "This is the most wonderful present any man could have. Thank you so very much, darling."

"You ought to thank Aunt Beatrice. She's the one who made it possible."

We therefore resolve to call the tractor Beatrice in her memory.

Clara is concerned that I have spent a significant portion of my inheritance in this way, yet she is mollified by the change she perceives in her son.

"I'll say this," she observes: "You've given him back his self-respect as a farmer, and I thank you for that."

There is regretfully a downside to this mechanisation. Neither our head carter, Jim Hobden, nor our remaining under-carter wants anything to do with it. They were both brought up in the age of the horse and consider themselves too old to adapt. Understandably perhaps, they regard our farm as a milk factory ruled by the internal combustion engine. This is alien to their culture. They have seen the sheep and pigs disappear while arable activity has diminished. Now the horses will be sold, and this is the last straw.

One of these two men would have had to be let go anyway to save money, but we should have liked the other to remain provided he would agree to drive one of the milk vans when I am nearly ready to have my baby. This has proved to be a forlorn hope, but we allow them both to stay on until they find new positions.

The under-carter has occupied our shepherd's cottage since the shepherd departed, and Jim has had a tied cottage here for many years. We shall therefore have two vacant dwellings and we have been wondering what to do with them. To be frank, they are mean little houses with no amenities and they would not easily find buyers. Bill, however, has taken a shine to Rosie, and it seems his passion has been requited. He approaches David one day and asks whether he might have the chance of a cottage.

Once the under-carter has made plans to move to a nearby farm we agree that Bill and Rosie should take up occupation of the shepherd's cottage following their marriage. This is a most satisfactory arrangement since Bill is an excellent worker and always willing to learn new skills. Rosie has been here for several years and has shown great adaptability. We are delighted that she has found a husband in a land so depleted of men.

Jim Hobden, too, finds a position suited to his experience, and so his cottage is now unoccupied. The future of this dwelling then takes an unexpected turn. I happen to mention its vacancy to Lilian in one of my letters, and this provokes an outpouring of enthusiasm for a weekend retreat. I tell her that, despite its having the advantage of being detached, the property is little more than a hovel – it would take great expense to make it habitable for someone like herself. She is adamant, however, and insists on coming down to see it. So Lilian visits us one weekend – the first time we have seen her in more than two years.

"Darlings, is it really that long? How time flies!"

I feel awfully guilty about Lilian. She has now made three films and I have not seen one of them.

"Don't be silly, darling – you've got a farm to run. You must work twelve hours a day, seven days a week!"

"Well, it's not quite that bad, Lilian, but I know what you mean."

Jim's old cottage is surrounded by garden, most of which has been cultivated to produce vegetables.

"Well," declares Lilian, "that will have to be relaid. I want roses and hollyhocks and things."

"The garden's scarcely the problem," I advise. "The house is really grim."

"Yes, but it's got character, darling. I mean a thorough refurbishment is not an impossibility, is it?"

"I suppose not if you've got money."

"Oh, I've got oodles of it, darling. You'll never guess what they pay me for doing a film: far more than for stage work. Perhaps I'll be a full-time film star. What do you think?"

"I think you'll miss your vocation. Films are just mime. You've got a wonderful singing voice and you're a superb stage actress."

"Flatterer!" she purrs while enjoying every accolade. "I'll give you £400."

"Lilian, this place is hardly worth half that in its present condition. We don't want to swindle you. Besides, it's really up to Clara and David."

Through her looks and theatrical manner Lilian has the ability to charm almost anyone, and it is finally agreed to accept her offer for the cottage. Given what I have spent on the tractor and plough, I suppose this must be seen as a welcome boost to our capital.

In the ensuing weeks the cottage is transformed into a rural hideaway for a burgeoning star of stage and screen who is becoming instantly recognisable wherever she goes. Despite her professional workload precluding many visits, I have seen several villagers peering in the direction of Honeysuckle Cottage in the hope of catching a glimpse of their famous neighbour.

With our two remaining carters gone and my pregnancy advancing, it is essential we find another van driver willing to adapt to a range of farming duties. Bill answers our prayer by recommending a village lad keen on mechanical things. His name is Frank. We teach him to drive and train him in the ways of delivering milk and eggs to domestic customers.

The advent of Beatrice necessitates conversion of our wagons and implements. Shafts are discarded for drawbars, the work being undertaken by our local blacksmith, who is beginning to adapt his business to new technology. Several of the wealthier residents have now purchased their first motor car, and a growing demand has arisen for servicing and repairs. Our smithy has therefore expanded into a garage, and the first petrol pump for miles has been installed.

Our tractor has become the talk of the village and farming community. It has not evoked widespread approval. Rural folk are suspicious of change and the word 'progress' is an anathema to many. There exists a long-term fear that horses may become extinct and we shall all perish in a netherworld of noise and exhaust fumes.

At Vine's Farm, however, Beatrice has become the lifeblood of our enterprise. She provides all the motive power and gives her driver, David, a new energy and dignity. Every field operation is completed in record time. This is particularly important during haymaking, where speed is a vital weapon against the vagaries of weather. Our two shire horses, Boxer and Cedric, have been sold. It was a sadness to see them go, but farming is a business, not a romantic notion.

At harvest the tractor again comes into its own. It does the work of three horses in pulling the binder, and does it more quickly. Now that ours is a horseless farm we have abandoned the sowing of oats in favour of barley. Another expense will be incurred through buying a rolling machine to crush the grain, but this can wait until after next year's harvest. The rolled barley will supplement hay and provide a concentrated feed for our beef cattle, which will then fatten faster. Unfortunately, this will not do for our dairy herd, which requires linseed cake to sustain the milk yield. The cake needs to be bought in, and this compromises our desire for self-sufficiency.

It is while David is busy ploughing fields destined for barley, at a speed hitherto undreamt of, that I give birth to my second baby on 19 September 1924. Oh dear – I do hope my husband will not be disappointed, for we now have a daughter. She has such a sweet little face and I am cradling her in my arms when David enters our bedroom and sees her for the first time. I need not have worried because I can see he adores the little mite, and I am sure she will grow up to become the apple of his eye. We name her Rebecca Clara after her two grandmothers. James Vere, now nearly three years old, comes in to meet his newly arrived sister and inspects her more out of curiosity than sibling love; yet I have no doubt he will grow into the protective brother we all wish.

Of course there are practical and financial implications in having a daughter. Most of James's hand-me-downs will be unsuitable. His pram, however, will once more be pressed into service, as will his pushchair in due course. I am so pleased these generous gifts from Lilian and Dotty will again be utilised.

At the end of September the Conservatives put down a vote of censure against the minority Labour government. Ramsay MacDonald suffers defeat, so Parliament is dissolved. A general election is set for 29 October – the fourth in less than six years – and I am still unqualified to vote despite being a twenty-four-year-old mother of two. I consider it an outrage! The Conservatives, having renounced tariff reform back in February, are well set to win, and they do so quite decisively with 412 seats. Stanley Baldwin is once again our Prime Minister.

CHAPTER 11

SPRING AWAKENING

I am now a full-time mother again, which at least gives me respite from the daily activities of farming. With winter well behind us, I take my newborn in the pram along country lanes where trees and hedgerows are sprouting forth their verdancy. It is a period of rebirth and hope for the future. Of course James Vere must not be neglected or allowed to think his baby sister has claimed all my affections. He is still too small to walk far, and I cannot manage his pushchair as well as the pram. So Clara comes to the rescue, and four of us set off to watch the season breathe new life into our countryside. Rufus, our cocker spaniel, accompanies us. He is restrained by a leash, which is an indignity for a gun dog, yet he seems to relish the occasion.

We pass Lilian's weekend cottage, which is now a tribute to man's contribution to renewal. Gone is the hovel-like meanness of this dwelling. It now bears the image of an idyllic rural retreat complete with its laid-out garden regularly tended by a retired labourer from the village. Daffodils in full bloom wave their heads in a gentle breeze as though to welcome us.

I only wish the beauty of our green and pleasant land could be matched by a buoyant economy. In the towns, and even more acutely in the country, life is a struggle. Within our own rural community there exists an underlying fear of business failure and foreclosure of loans. People are putting a brave face on it all, but the spectre of catastrophe casts a dark shadow over their enterprise.

I do not wish to boast, but at Vine's Farm, whether through innate pessimism or astuteness, we predicted a downturn in fortunes following a return to peace. Forewarned is forearmed, as one might say, so we have made what preparations we can to stave off the worst concomitants of falling income. I have to admit that we have also been fortunate. Owing to Lord Cloudsley's kindness, we were able to purchase our holding at a larger than expected discount. Aunt Beatrice's legacy and Lilian's generosity in buying the cottage have made major contributions as we seek to transform our business through investment.

We have expanded our dairy herd, and there are now four mobile poultry houses folded over grassland. Our farm is almost all about milk and eggs and selling as much of this produce as we can directly to the consumer. Our beef cattle, which scarcely make a profit, are refugees from the dairy: heifers, not considered suitable for breeding, and castrated bull calves. These we rear and fatten for the pot. As they are dairy shorthorns, rather than one of the beef breeds, they fetch the worst prices at market; but at least they are animals born on the farm and not purchased by us for cash.

We shall soon be selling virtually nothing from our small corn harvest. Barley is being grown to feed the beef cattle, and its straw provides bedding. Any surplus grain will be sold, but there is little money in it. We grow a small acreage of kale, which we cut by hand during winter to provide green fodder for the cows while they are housed. Our pastures on impervious Weald clay are too wet for winter grazing. Would that they grew on a free-draining soil; then perhaps we could dispense with kale as we have dispensed with so many other arable crops. David, however, points out that kale is a good feed and, as grass growth is so minimal in winter, we should probably have insufficient for our needs without it. So while the cows tread straw into useful manure they receive a diet of hay, kale and linseed cake, thereby providing us with valuable milk in return.

With the war now over for six and a half years, and a tractor to give him mobility, David has begun to loosen his tongue on the conflict. He spares us the unpleasant details, but seems willing to discuss related events.

My father has bought his first motor car – an Austin Seven. I joke that it is not unlike Rebecca's pram, differing only in that it does not require pushing and accommodates *two* rather large babies!

One Sunday my parents drive over to join us for lunch at Vine's Farm. During dessert David poses a theory about the war.

"Have any of you thought what might have happened if succession to the British Crown had been determined by primogeniture?"

"That's a very big word, David," remarks my mother.

"Enough to give anyone indigestion," quips my father.

"Well, come on," David insists. "Have you thought about it?"

"Can't say I have, old man," my father adds nonchalantly.

David seems resigned to developing the argument himself.

"I take it you all know what primogeniture means?" he asks with a tinge of irritability.

"Yes, David," I reply. "We all know."

"Well, if we'd had it – primogeniture, that is – when Queen Victoria died, who would have succeeded to the throne?"

"Her eldest child, of course," my father advises.

"Who was?"

"Well, it was Princess Victoria, wasn't it?" my mother suggests.

"Exactly," confirms David.

At this point James Vere, his chin barely visible above the table, makes a mess with his bread-and-butter pudding. I clear it up.

"So Princess Vicky would have become queen," my husband asserts.

"She wouldn't have reigned for very long," Clara interjects. "She died herself a few months after the old lady went; she was too ill even to attend her mother's funeral."

"Yes," continues David triumphantly, "and who would have become King of England then?"

"Her eldest child," my father repeats, "just as before."

"And who was that?" David persists.

There is an eerie silence at the table.

"Yes, you all know, don't you?" says my husband as though he is about to reveal the culprit in some cheap detective novel.

"Kaiser Bill," admits Clara. "I'd scarcely thought about it. Makes you wonder, doesn't it?"

"It certainly does, Mother. Look at the situation in 1914. The German kaiser and English king would have been one and the same person. Now what would that have meant? Would he have gone to war with himself? I hardly think so. So what would have happened? Anyone got any ideas? How about you, father-in-law?"

My father empties his mouth before answering: "I think we might have been on the same side and defeated France in a pincer movement."

"You may be right," David concedes. "But suppose he decided that Germany should fight the French alone? After all, he was hoping to defeat them quickly with the Schlieffen Plan before turning his entire forces against Russia. No country wants to fight on two fronts. The Schlieffen Plan meant invading Belgium to attack France. Britain was allied to Belgium, and could hardly have taken up arms against her. So my theory is that if King Willie had sat on our throne, we shouldn't have got involved in the war at all!"

"It's all ifs and buts, David," I counter. "For one thing, it's our government which decides whether to declare war, not our monarch."

"A King Wilhelm might have withheld the royal assent," my husband asserts.

"It's water under the bridge now," sighs my mother. "As much as we might like to have changed things, we can't."

"Yes," returns David, "but can't you all see how something relatively trivial, such as primogeniture, can cause our country so much upheaval? Ten per cent of our male population who fought were wiped out – gone for ever – and I wouldn't have this blasted leg wound!"

There is no adequate answer one can give to someone in David's position who endured suffering and saw so many of his comrades cut down.

On a much brighter note I should record that Bill and Rosie have married, and they are now happily ensconced in the cottage we promised them. They are long-term employees, and we feel we can depend on them to adapt to any farming changes which may need to be made. Our second van driver, Frank, looks up to Bill and tries to follow his example so maybe we shall come to regard him, too, as a dependable employee for many years to come.

Once the barley is cut, we purchase a corn-rolling machine which can be driven by a belt from the tractor pulley. This new acquisition is pressed into service as soon as our crop is threshed and our beef cattle begin to enjoy an enhanced diet.

Another concession to modernity has emerged in our rural community. The main road through our village has been resurfaced with tarmacadam. We now have a smooth ride all the way to the local market town. What a blessing this is, not only for comfort, but also for a greatly reduced incidence of punctures! Motorised vehicles are gradually replacing the horse, although motor traffic is still very occasional here.

The months pass and we move into 1926 and anticipate a new spring to awaken the countryside from its winter slumber. On 11 March a royal commission under the chairmanship of Sir Herbert Samuel reports on the mining industry. It proposes several measures to improve working conditions, such as pithead baths at some indeterminate future date. The only recommendation for immediate implementation, however, is a wage reduction. The miners' union secretary, A. J. Cook, has responded with the words "Not a penny off the pay, not a second on the day." This unlikely contributor to verse is clearly displeased, and industrial unrest is in the air.

The apparent impasse culminates in the General Strike on 3 May – not quite the spring awakening for which we had hoped. Even from our rural perspective, however, I think it only right that miners should have a living wage, and for this principle so many other trade unions have struck in sympathy. From the self-interest point of view, we are fortunate that volunteer drivers have manned milk trains – virtually the only trains to run. Hence our wholesale milk is transported from our local station as normal.

Sir Herbert Samuel now drafts proposals for a National Wages Board in the mining industry. This authority would be empowered to cut wages, but only when the Samuel Commission's other recommendations are adopted. The TUC General Council is satisfied with this suggestion, and it calls off the national strike on 12 May. This is a great relief.

The most noticeable thing in our small community is that the trains are running normally again. The miners, however, are dissatisfied and they continue their industrial action. For the householder this causes no hardship since there is scarcely any need to heat one's home at this season of the year.

By the time it is necessary to replenish one's coal bunker the miners are driven back to work through starvation. They were on strike for six months, and now they have had to accept lower wages and longer hours. If one is going to withdraw one's labour, then it might be expedient to choose the most appropriate moment.

Although it is easy to bemoan one's lot in agriculture, my heart does go out to our subterranean workers, who face danger and discomfort as well as little reward. At least we have fresh air to breathe, home-grown food and plentiful wood to burn in our hearths.

CHAPTER 12

THROUGH THE LOOKING GLASS

1927 dawns, and my older child, James Vere, is now five years old and ready to start school. Our finances do not stretch to paying educational fees, so David and I are resigned to placing our son in the village council's seat of learning. My parents, however, then demonstrate their generosity by offering assistance whereby James can attend a preparatory institution set in nearby countryside. This is most convenient in that the school is situated en route to our local market town.

I have therefore taken to driving our newer van on the milk round again, dropping off James on the way and collecting him when I return during the afternoon. I am so grateful to my parents because the class sizes are very small and my son is flourishing under the individual attention he receives.

Little Rebecca is nearly two and a half and running about the house, her progress checked by the seemingly austere figure of her grandmother. My daughter keeps asking, "Where James go?" Clara has to repeat the fact that he is at school, where all little girls also have to go when they are five. Rebecca's linguistic skills are still somewhat limited, so she just shrugs her shoulders and resumes playing.

Prices for agricultural produce continue to fall unabated, and this year is proving to be a poor one for both weather and crops. We hear from time to time how old so and so from somewhere yonder has gone bankrupt. Vine's Farm, however, manages to keep its head above water thanks to milk production.

It is because we have increased our dairy enterprise over some years that we have now reached a crossroads. One person is required for every ten cows milked by hand; so if we are to expand any further, then we shall have to think seriously about purchasing a miking machine. Our daily sale of bottled milk to the public has now exceeded fifty gallons, and hand-bottling is proving too onerous. Thus bottling machinery is also being seen as a consideration.

It seems that as farming incomes decline, we are virtually compelled to spend increasing sums on automation. There is no Lilian or Aunt Beatrice to bail us out this time, so we have to count our pennies. We have no immediate prospect of electricity being laid on – hence any machinery we do buy will have to be powered by an oil engine. Fortunately, we already have a portable one used to operate the hay-and-straw elevator.

In the wake of sighs of resignation, the day arrives when we take delivery of milking and bottling machinery bought on 'easy terms' over two years. David calls this hire-purchase system the 'glad and sorry', but we have done our arithmetic and calculate that our income is sufficient to pay the instalments as agreed.

In a shed abutting our milking parlour the oil engine, by means of a belt, drives a vacuum pump. This provides suction to teat cups, which suck milk from the cows. A safety valve, fitted to a pipe from the vacuum pump, is set to control the suction pressure to a maximum of fourteen pounds per square inch, thereby simulating a calf's sucking ability. In the same time it takes one man to hand-milk ten cows, George Akehurst and an assistant can milk sixty animals with this new apparatus. It is fantastic! We find ourselves saying, "Why didn't we do this before?" The answer is, of course, that we could not afford it.

With automation providing David and me with a little more time to ourselves, we elect to do something we have always planned, but never got around to. The solitary cinema in our market town is showing one of Lilian's films. So, with James and Rebecca tucked safely in their beds and Clara to look after them, we journey into town by van and settle in front of the silver screen with expectation.

This is a whole new experience for me. It is quite unlike the theatre, for films are silent and the only sound, provided by the management, is a lady playing the piano. I joke with David that, if I had not met him, then I might have earned my living in this way. One matter for which I was not prepared is the element of audience participation as people react to events depicted on the screen. David tells me that in the earliest days of cinema – when, for example, a train appeared to come straight towards them – people would scream and dive for cover. It seems that audiences are now inured to such stimuli and are capable of responding with indifference. Silence, however, appears not to be an option.

Lilian looks as marvellous as ever on-screen despite being displayed in monochrome. I am full of concern for her though, as I am transported into another world projected before my eyes. Her character is being stalked by a serial killer. Eventually he corners her in an ill-lit room and the terror feigned through her countenance and body movements is so realistic that I want to rush to the front, demanding this fiend leaves my old school chum alone. David senses my emotion and whispers in my ear, "It's only a film, you know."

During late July, just after Endacott College has broken up for the summer vacation, there is to be an old girls' reunion. These events are held every so often, but circumstances have prevented my attending any until now. This will give me an opportunity to see Lilian in the flesh again. She and Dotty are to stay at Honeysuckle Cottage for a few days, and I am to journey with them to Endacott. It transpires that Lilian is now a motorist, and she is to bring Dotty with her from London. On the day of reunion they will pick me up at Vine's Farm.

Lilian's car is a Lagonda. She tells me, as though she is some kind of motor engineer, that it is the latest model – a 16/65. Lilian explains further that the 2.7-litre engine has six cylinders, with overhead valves, and produces 17.7 horsepower. I only know that it seems far too powerful for her with its throaty roar and capacity to frighten the living daylights out of me. It is a warm summer's afternoon and the fabric hood has been lowered so an air current generated by the vehicle thrills our sensibilities. We are all wearing hats – which is just as well, as otherwise our hair on arrival would resemble hay in a cow's manger.

When we reach Endacott, mercifully in one piece, my mind is filled immediately with nostalgia. I realise this is the first occasion I have been here since that day in 1918 when I left school and embarked upon life as a woman. How the passage of time does transform one! I wonder whether other school acquaintances I have not seen for nine years will seem like different people. Shall I appear different to them?

We enter our alma mater by the main entrance – an access forbidden to us as pupils. Here we are confronted by the formidable bust of the founder, Miss Ernestine Endacott. My intended double entendre is scarcely inappropriate! It is a tradition that old girls, when entering the building, stroke the founder's head as though to demonstrate affection for the one who made such a wonderful education possible. The three of us cannot do so without giggling almost disrespectfully, and Dotty accentuates our flippancy by stroking that part of Miss Endacott's anatomy which first comes to prominence.

"Well, at least nobody's put a chamber pot on her head!" observes Lilian impishly.

My amusement is reduced and finally extinguished when I notice a tribute to Edith Nixon, the one old girl who perished in the service of her country during the Great War. There are three photographs of Edith provided by her family: one as a schoolgirl at Endacott, another as a young woman in 1913, and another in her VAD uniform just weeks before she was killed. I feel tears welling up in my eyes. What a waste of a young life! Yet she died trying to save others, and I sense that, if she had to be lost, then this is how she would have chosen to go.

I turn round, and to my amazement I see the school swot of old – Millicent Harper. She has not changed a bit. She looked middle-aged at school; she still looks middle-aged; and I do not doubt she will look middle-aged when she is ninety, in which case she will have had the last laugh on us all.

"Isn't that you, Vera?" she enquires as though to emphasise the notion that I have aged to my detriment.

"Millicent!" I respond. "You haven't changed a bit."

"I'm still at school, so I suppose that's why," she remarks as though to induce humour.

I give a silly laugh.

"You see, I teach here now," she explains: "classics."

"You came straight from Cambridge?"

"Yes, I got a first."

"I never doubted it."

"There's afternoon tea outside on the terrace."

"How lovely! Shall we go, girls?"

Dotty, Lilian and I repair to the terrace for refreshment, and we are reunited with a few old friends with whom we exchange life stories. I am profoundly moved by the high proportion who are still unmarried, and remind myself how lucky I am to have David and two children.

What is more poignant is to observe the younger element, who left Endacott some years later than my contemporaries. A far higher proportion of these girls are married already – no doubt to men not yet of military age when the armistice was signed. They are very different to the class of 1918, despite being younger by only a few years. They dress differently, act differently and everything seems to be 'madly gay, ducky'. These are the modern women, the bright young things, the flappers. Skirts are just below the knee, their wearers having a vitality noticeably absent in what I call 'my generation' – the lost generation. I suddenly feel rather old, despite being only twenty-seven. The Charleston is not for me.

Miss Buckmaster, who must be nearing sixty, is still in post as headmistress. She identifies Dotty, Lilian and me as we sip tea together.

"Well, if it isn't the three little maids from school, as W. S. Gilbert might have put it," she quips as though to engage our appreciation. "Let me see – are you still little maids?"

"Vera is married," advises Dotty.

I confirm this revelation by displaying my wedding ring.

"So I see," responds Miss Buckmaster. "Do you have children, Vera?"

"Yes, two. My son started school in January; he's five. My daughter will be three in September."

"Indeed, so will you be sending her to us here at Endacott when she is five? We're not exactly cradle-to-grave, but with our new junior department we can now educate a girl throughout her school career."

"Isn't five dreadfully young to board a child?" I enquire.

"Oh, well, we don't board girls until they are at least eight, but the advent of the motor car allows our little ones to come on a daily basis," Miss Buckmaster explains as though leaving no stone unturned in extolling the virtues of her establishment.

"I'm not sure we could afford the fees unless my father would help us out. He did so for my son. . . ."

"Then I am sure he will come up trumps for your daughter, Vera. Now that we are in the twentieth century, and entitled to vote, men have to understand that the education of women is just as important as their own scholarship."

"We're twenty-seven," interjects Lilian, "and we still can't vote."

Dotty and I nod in frustrated agreement.

"Patience, girls, patience," returns Miss Buckmaster. "It can't be long now before all women over twenty-one will have the franchise. Now, Lilian, you have been a busy bee. You must be our most celebrated old girl – theatre, films! I even saw your picture in a magazine, advertising soap!"

"I like to think of myself as a clean-living person," jokes Lilian.

Our former headmistress gives a high-pitched laugh. "I thought, Lilian," she asserts, "that being one of our prettiest girls you would be amongst the first to embrace matrimony."

"I seem to be married to my career, Miss Buckmaster. The work keeps coming my way and I feel I must make hay while the sun shines."

Dotty laughs loudly.

"Is that funny, Dorothy?" queries Miss Buckmaster.

"Well, yes, it is really. You see, Vera is a farmer's wife."

"Oh," replies the headmistress as though I have suddenly fallen from grace, "so you married a farmer, Vera?"

"Yes."

"I take it he's a landowner, then?"

"We're buying the farm on a mortgage."

Miss Buckmaster half nods, indicating she is not quite sure as to our social status, and turns to Dotty: "What are you doing now, Dorothy?"

"I'm a secretary."

"To whom?"

"The owner of a London firm supplying machine tools."

Miss Buckmaster's face wears a puzzled countenance as though machine tools are totally outside her experience.

"Have you met Millicent Harper this afternoon?" she enquires. We all nod.

"She teaches classics now, here at Endacott."

"Yes, she told me," I confirm.

"She attained a first-class degree from Girton College, Cambridge," beams Miss Buckmaster with pride.

"Yes, she told me that too," I add.

"One of our cleverest girls, you know. I tell all our pupils how they should try to emulate Millicent. At Endacott we believe we can irrigate the most arid of deserts and no girl must feel devoid of aspiration."

I cannot think why any girl should wish to be like Millicent, but I am not a headmistress who measures everything by the academic prowess of my students.

Miss Buckmaster moves away to converse with other alumnae and we three try not to convey our mirth to the assembled company. We giggle into our cups as we pretend to drink tea already consumed.

On our way home we analyse whether we were ever regarded as arid deserts, and, if so, whether our esteemed headmistress now considers us to have become irrigated.

"I don't feel particularly wet, do you?" asks Dotty.

"I'm so dry I'm not sure I can make it to the oasis in time!" Lilian comments.

"Ooh, look," I observe. "There's hope for us all. It's beginning to rain!"

We stop to raise the hood of Lilian's Lagonda, laughing like schoolgirls as we seek to protect ourselves from the worsening shower. The task completed, we dive for cover and continue our journey in the highest of spirits.

I enjoyed our excursion back to Endacott. It gave me some respite from concerns about Vine's Farm, but now I must return to matters both domestic and economic.

I read in the farming press that every £1,000 invested in agriculture during 1920 has now depreciated by seventy-five per cent. Truly I find this a horrifying statistic, and I ask David how long such a trend can continue. He contends that anything functional has some value, and eventually the situation will bottom out.

What is an obvious truth is that, like so many others, we purchased our holding at a market peak and have watched our capital diminish through no fault of our own. My husband says that we have to stick it out. When the market reaches its nadir, so the theory goes, our industry will begin to recover. Cynically, David remarks that the government will then pass some innocuous legislation and claim this has saved the future of British farming.

Seeing one's own capital depreciate is bad enough. One can just grit one's teeth and wait for recovery. What is so frightening is the depreciation of borrowed capital, and this fear is clearly pertinent to us. We obtained a mortgage from the bank to buy Vine's Farm when times were good. Now it seems our collateral has diminished in value to the point where it is worth less than the sum advanced.

In 1919 we purchased our farm for £4,500. If the holding now is worth only a quarter of what it was eight years ago, then its present value is £1,125. We borrowed £3,000!

I remember my father telling me of the danger that security devaluation can trigger a mortgagee to demand that the mortgager pays a cash sum to make good the deficit. David advises me, however, that whereas money invested in farming has on average depreciated by three-quarters, land values have only halved – as if this is not bad enough!

So, if the bank revalued our farm at £2,250, where should we stand? Our lenders may say that they would be willing to continue advancing two-thirds of this sum, but require us to pay one-third in return. In short, they would demand a cash settlement of £750 to preserve the mortgage. We do not have anywhere near such a sum to pay away into thin air just like that!

Frankly, I am terrified. To date the bank has not required the farm to be revalued. Perhaps it is impressed with our business model. Impressed or not, agricultural economics generally are so dire that surely it is only a question of time before our lenders act.

Recently I have noticed posters appearing which advertise impending farm-dispersal sales. This suggests to me that various banks have indeed imposed revaluations and foreclosed on loans where the farmer cannot pay a lump sum to retain his mortgage. In other parts of the country, where the main corn-growing areas lie, the situation must be much worse. Here in Sussex, with its preponderance of livestock and mixed farming, there exists a better chance of survival.

If it were only I who stood to lose by this aura of doom, then I should shoulder the burden with greater fortitude. It is when I see my two young children playing innocently about the house and farm that I fear for our future. It is my responsibility to provide them with a secure and predictable environment, and I dread letting them down. My concerns, however, do not end there. My poor, wounded husband, who risked everything for his country, is also vulnerable, together with his ageing mother, for whom Vine's Farm has been a home for so long.

'I blame you, Vera Coulthurst, with your fancy ideas about buying the farm, borrowing money, purchasing vans, a tractor with plough, rolling machine, milking machine, bottling machinery and anything else you can think of. You have risen above your station, young lady, and it is not that you have been without luck: your father, Aunt Beatrice, Lilian . . .'

I am alone at this moment, and I am crying, not for myself, but because of myself. It would serve me right if David, Clara and my parents were to berate me for my foolishness. Perhaps this is what I need – people to take me down a peg or two and remind me that I am not even half so clever as I sometimes think I am.

CHAPTER 13

THE LOST GENERATION

If meekness betrays insecurity, then my innermost thoughts cannot be concealed from David, who remarks upon my subdued disposition of late.

"You're not your usual ebullient self," he observes.

I cannot deny his analysis.

"What's troubling you, darling?"

"Can't you guess?"

"Not this mortgage business again?"

"How can I think of anything else?"

"If you don't, there could be a self-fulfilling prophecy."

I tell my husband that we have the Sword of Damocles hanging over us. He tries to comfort me by pointing out that the bank has never made any attempt to contact us about our loan, and consequently it must be satisfied we are a sound risk.

Our situation has not been helped by the fact that we have had to purchase another oil engine. George Akehurst cannot milk cows at the same time we wish to use the hay-and-straw elevator if we have only one engine. So the portable one already in our possession reverts solely to elevator duties while George has been supplied with a larger, standing engine to power the milking machine. Is there no end to the amount of equipment we have to buy to enable the farm to function efficiently?

"It's just spend, spend, spend, David. A farm seems to soak up money faster than a blotting pad soaks up ink!"

It is, however, an inescapable truth that no matter how perilous one assumes one's own position to be, there is always somebody in a worse situation.

My son's school has broken up for the Christmas holiday, so I take a rest, not merely from delivering him to his seat of learning, but also from delivering milk. Bill and Frank are driving the vans and I find myself looking after James and Rebecca while David is busy at his desk catching up with paperwork. I take a few seconds to reflect on our domestic life, which, apart from financial worries, is something of a rural idyll. There is no animosity between anyone in our household, and my children bring laughter and contentment in equal measure. This encourages me to believe that David and I are fulfilling our role as parents. Clara has always had a sternness about her, yet she exudes human qualities which command respect. Everyone knows that beneath the façade lies a kind heart.

I glance out from the parlour window and observe the winter chill through defoliated trees and dead leaves scurrying about our garden. Inside, warmth provided by a log fire insulates us from the harshness of the elements. James and Rebecca (or Becky, as we have become accustomed to calling her) are playing with their toys – not expensive ones purchased in a shop, but ones fashioned by my husband's inventive hands. He has made Becky a wonderful doll's house and is gradually helping her to furnish it with miniature chairs, tables and beds. James has a wooden lorry which tips up together with various other vehicles which David has constructed over the years. My children have placed their orders with St Nicholas for the coming festive season, but it will be St David who will bring them to fruition.

Suddenly, my equanimity is shattered by a frantic banging at the front door. Clara minds the children while I go to answer it. I am seized by an instant foreboding at the sight of our caller. This would not normally be the case as Muriel Pateman, our neighbour at Mill Farm, is a dear friend. She married her husband, John, just before the war. They are in their thirties and have two boys aged eight and six. Like David, John volunteered in 1914. He reached the rank of sergeant in the Royal Sussex Regiment and came through the conflict unscathed. John and Muriel bought their farm from Lord Cloudsley about the same time as we did, and they have run it as a mixed enterprise ever since. Muriel is a no-nonsense person, so I am deeply disturbed by her emotional appeareance.

"Come in from the cold," I tell her.

She almost collapses into my arms. Her cheeks are tear-stained and virtually drained of colour. She is shaking like a leaf and unable to speak. I do not want my children to see her in this condition, so I usher her into our dining room and sit her down, my arm around her shoulders.

"Now, come on, Muriel – what is the matter?"

She can seemingly only utter one indistinct word, which sounds like 'barn'. I ask her to wait while I fetch David.

"It's the only word I can get out of her."

"Well, what's happened?" he enquires. "Has it caught fire or something?"

"I don't know, but would you go and look? Don't risk your leg. Drive over there."

"The vans are still out on the milk round."

"Then take the tractor."

"I can't go on the road with spade lugs."

"Go round the field edges. There's a stile between our farm and theirs. It's only a very short walk from there."

If David tells me the ground is too wet, I fear I shall scream! I inform Clara of events.

"You mind the children," she demands. "I'll make some tea." Our internal walls are thin enough to hear Clara's stentorian voice from another room. "Drink this down you. What's all this about? Big girl like you weeping buckets everywhere!"

Despite her direct approach, Clara is unable to elicit any further information. We have to await David's return, heralded by the familiar sound of Beatrice's chugging engine. When my husband reappears in the house his face is ashen, and that epithet bears no reference to any fire.

"It's John," he reveals.

"Has he had an accident?" I query. "Is he all right?"

"I'm afraid he's dead, darling. Four years in the trenches couldn't get him; now he's dead."

"Dead?" I respond incredulously. "How?"

David pauses.

"He took his twelve-bore into the barn and blew his brains out!"

107

I cannot speak. I cannot think, save for the fact that the last thing we want is two weeping women in one house.

"Why?" is ultimately the only response I can give.

David hands me a piece of paper.

"I found this sticking out of his pocket."

I read it with trembling fingers. It is a letter from John's bank – the same bank as ours.

"They've foreclosed on his loan," David confirms.

"Foreclosed?" I repeat in disbelief. "But surely they would have asked for a liquid sum to preserve the loan before foreclosing?"

"Perhaps they did and he couldn't come up with the cash."

"But when I asked Poppa about this he said the bank might continue with a loan even if the borrower doesn't pay such a demand – something about not wanting to be landed with a property they couldn't sell at a high enough price to recover their money."

"Maybe it was worse than that. John might have defaulted on his repayments. That would probably trigger a foreclosure."

Despite the awfulness of this situation, selfishness begins to dominate my thoughts as I consider the ramifications for ourselves. Mill Farm today; so why not Vine's Farm tomorrow? David shakes me out of my contemplations.

"What about the two boys?"

I look at my watch. It is a quarter to three.

"They'll be at school," I reply. "The council schools haven't broken up yet. Oh dear – they'll be walking home before long."

"Then one of us will have to head them off and bring them here."

"I'll do it, David. As soon as the first milk van's back, you go and summon the constable and doctor to Mill Farm. Then try and get the vicar to come here."

As I walk along the road towards the village, huddled against the cold, I try to think how I should handle matters with Muriel's two sons. They are cheery boys who rarely cease telling everyone how they both wish to become farmers when they grow up. It is highly debatable now whether their aspirations will ever be realised; and even if they are, there will be no future at Mill Farm.

I arrive in time to greet them as they emerge from the school gate.

"Hello, Mrs Coulthurst. What are you doing here?"

I have a lump in my throat which refuses to dissipate.

"Oh, your mummy's having tea with us, so I've come to fetch you. Do you like sticky buns?"

"Coo, yes."

I feel such a wretched fraud, but what else can I do?" I believe that I must keep up this pretence until we are ensconced in the warmth and privacy of my home. My task is made all the more difficult through the children maintaining a conversation about their school day and preparations for Christmas. Why did this tragedy have to happen as the festive season approaches? For two small boys it is going to be a rotten Christmas, and I am powerless to prevent it.

Why, oh why could John Pateman not have shared his problems with us before embarking upon such a destructive path to end his agony? Perhaps he was too proud to admit his failure to others, or maybe the war so damaged his defence mechanisms that only departure from this troubled world could bring him relief.

I cannot bear to relate the scene which ensued at Vine's Farm upon our arrival that afternoon. It was not my husband – my children's father – who had taken his own life, yet I felt and still do feel the pangs of loss, tragedy and futility which must always accompany such an event.

I could not let Muriel and her boys return home that day. Indeed, they stayed with us for a rather sombre Christmas. How I wished that Lilian and Dotty could have joined us! But Lilian was juggling film work while starring in a West End play, and Dotty was visiting her parents.

So now 1928 has emerged from the despair of recent days. I hope it will augur well for us.

CHAPTER 14

LAND

A sale is held at Mill Farm in which Muriel's livestock and deadstock come under the hammer. It is customary in such auctions for neighbouring farmers to increase the bidding in an attempt to help the outgoing family. I see little evidence of this now as everyone is cutting his expenditure in the interests of survival. Nobody wishes to pay more for a lot than it is worth.

Muriel and her young sons cannot bear to witness the bidding as everything for which her late husband worked is systematically sold. One observes the dismantling of a dream. Something which has taken years to assemble is now being undone in a single morning. One by one animals and implements are purchased and led or carted away, leaving an empty steading devoid of activity – a soulless shell of a farm now awaiting only the human occupants to vacate it.

The remnants of the Pateman family go to live with Muriel's unmarried sister in a nearby town. They aren't willing urbanites, yet at least they have shelter. When all their debts are settled there is precious little capital left, and the indications are that Muriel will have to seek any employment she can find. It is a stark reminder to me of what lies ahead for victims of economic failure, and I sense a bitter chill running down my spine.

The bank now holds all the equity in Mill Farm. This financial institution is a farm owner by accident rather than by design, and the holding is immediately put on the market. A large board advertising its offer for sale is erected near the farm entrance. It remains there for weeks and then months.

David opines that now is a good time for a man to embark upon a career as a yeoman farmer because he can obtain a property at a fraction of the price we would have had to pay during the immediate aftermath of war. In reality, however, few men see the present condition of British agriculture as auguring well for the future. Even farmers' sons are tending to eschew a rural life in favour of more secure employment in the professions.

The workforce at Mill Farm has been drastically cut by the bank. Only a few men have been retained to manage growing crops and keep the holding in some sort of order. There are no animals whatsoever; it is like a ghost farm.

I feel so sorry for any agricultural worker who is made redundant, particularly if he is nearing retirement. The spectre of the workhouse is yet to be eradicated from our society, and men without extended family are certainly vulnerable to its tentacles.

A little personal joy comes my way in April. Amidst the excitement of a public political meeting the Home Secretary, Sir William Joynson-Hicks, blurts out a promise which one suspects has not received prior blessing from the Cabinet. He commits himself to lowering the voting age for women from thirty to twenty-one, thus giving us parity with men. The government has felt obliged to honour his promise, so an Act is passed to grant what everyone seems to be calling the 'flapper vote'. I am certainly no flapper, and I have already celebrated my twenty-eighth birthday, so all this is rather late for me; but I may yet get the opportunity to vote in one general election before I am thirty. Sir William is known by the sobriquet 'Jix', so I shall be charitable and say "Hoorah for Jix!"

My elation is somewhat short-lived as David soon receives a letter from the bank. It is the correspondence we have been dreading. Our mortgagees are requesting that we pay £750 to preserve our loan agreement. Coming in the wake of the Pateman disaster, this demand is shattering notwithstanding its expectation. That evening I take the letter to my father and tearfully await his reaction to its contents.

"Try not to distress yourself, my dear," he says gently. "You may remember my telling you that many people receiving such a communication will have to decline, and the bank will have little option but to let things ride in the current economic climate."

"They didn't let things ride with the Patemans," I protest.

"I think you would find their situation was fundamentally different to your own."

"So what are we going to do, Poppa?"

"Leave this letter with me and I'll compose a response on my legal practice's headed notepaper. If you and David approve its contents, then you can send it to the bank in the envelope I provide and await developments."

Sometimes I do not know what I should do without my beloved father's advice. He is always as good as his word, and within twenty-four hours David and I are reading his contribution to our cause.

Dear Sirs,

We act for D. R. Coulthurst, Esq. of Vine's Farm.

We understand that, as mortgagees of this property, you have revalued it in the sum of £2,250, this being 50% of the £4,500 for which our client purchased the holding in 1919.

We should point out that our client obtained the property at a discount, the true market value in 1919 being circa £6,000. In consequence, using your own formula, the market value now would be in the region of £3,000.

Under the terms of the mortgage in 1919 you advanced our client £3,000 – i.e. two-thirds of the purchase price. You now request that our client pays you a lump sum of £750 (being one-third of your current valuation) to sustain the mortgage agreement.

Since the current market value exceeds your revaluation by an equivalent amount of £750, we submit that your interests are preserved through not requiring our client to pay any cash sum at this juncture.

We should also draw your attention to the fact that our client has never defaulted on any mortgage repayments and that he has adapted his business to take account of changing market conditions. Indeed, his milk and egg retailing activity is producing profit in a general climate of agricultural depression.

We further submit therefore that our client represents a very small risk and, one might even say, a good proposition for your bank.

We look forward to receiving a positive response from you in due course.

Yours faithfully,

The correspondence is passed to Clara, who examines it through her spectacles.

"Your father writes a very clever letter," she concludes at length.

"I'd say it's a damn good one," adds David.

"Shall we send it, then?" I ask.

Unanimously we agree it would be folly not to, so into the village pillar box it goes.

In the days ahead we can think of little else, and we discharge our farming duties in an almost perfunctory manner. Three weeks pass, and still there is silence from the bank. We begin to wonder whether my father's letter was delivered or if a reply has similarly been delayed or even lost in the post. Perhaps our lenders are waiting to hear from us or, worse, are convinced we are just burying our heads in the sand. Maybe they are planning some horrible retribution for ignoring them. I tremble every time the postman calls. On each occasion when the dreaded reply does not land on our front doormat I am unsure whether to be relieved or to renew my fear.

Eventually the justification or redundancy of my trepidation is about to be determined. I recognise the buff-coloured typewritten envelope lying inside our front entrance waiting for someone to summon the courage to pick it up. It is addressed to David, so I pass it to him with a barely disguised shaking hand. He opens it and withdraws the letter contained therein. He studies it carefully.

"Well?" I enquire.

"They want to see me."

"Don't they say why?"

"No."

I am not sure whether to be angry or to burst into tears. In the event I remain just confused. David is likewise disposed.

"They've suggested an appointment at 2.30 p.m. next Thursday."

"Nothing else?" I query.

David hands me the letter.

"This is too bad," I protest. "Don't they know what this must be doing to us?"

"I don't suppose they care, darling. It's just business to them."

"Bloody monkey business!" I exclaim, using language alien to my nature.

The fact is, of course, that we must continue waiting except for dispatching an acceptance of the proffered appointment. In an attempt to assuage my frustration I seek further counsel from my father, who tries to placate me by observing that the bank has not responded negatively to his submissions.

When Thursday arrives David and I elect to take the train to our nearby market town. The vans are out delivering milk, so there is scarcely any choice. A short walk from the town station brings us to our bank. Once inside, we are asked to sit down and wait while the manager is apprised of our attendance. His secretary seems surprised that I am even there, and she is almost shocked when I rise to be shown into her superior's office along with my husband.

The manager stands courteously to greet David and appears unsettled by my presence. I fully expect him to enquire whether I might be more comfortable waiting outside with a cup of tea. In the event all three of us are brought tea by the secretary, who eyes me suspiciously as though I have breached some male bastion like an erstwhile suffragette. I ignore her, buoyed by the knowledge that the franchise has been extended to me, albeit belatedly.

"Biscuit?" queries the manager as he holds out a plate of somewhat primitive fare.

I begin to wonder whether this refreshment is a prelude to some devastating revelation which our host is trying to mitigate.

"Now, Mr Coulthurst and, er, Mrs Coulthurst, we received a letter from your solicitors. I note you're clients of Stansfield, Pearson & Partners, undoubtedly one of our most respected local legal firms."

I nearly blurt out that Charles Stansfield is my father, but quickly button my lip lest the manager, Mr Lamacraft, assumes the case we have made is somehow vitiated. I pray that David does not let the cat out of the bag. Mercifully, he remains silent.

"The bank has discussed this correspondence in some detail," Mr Lamacraft continues, "and I'm pleased to inform you that we envisage making no extraneous financial demands upon you as things stand. Indeed, as your solicitors point out, we are really quite impressed, Mr Coulthurst, at the way in which you have adapted your business to suit current market conditions. Instead of just bemoaning your lot, as many farmers do when times are challenging, you have swallowed your pride and sought out retail opportunities for your produce."

"Actually, that was my wife's idea," David confesses.

Mr Lamacraft looks nonplussed.

"Er, really? Well, that's fascinating." He projects a forced smile in my direction. "As I was saying, Mr Coulthurst, you have not thought going into trade was beneath you. I am rather irritated by those persons who think being in trade is somewhat *infra dignitatem*. I don't think I'm speaking out of turn if I say that many of our credit customers are tradespeople whether they sell at the door or from behind a counter. Trade is the economic backbone of this country. Even Napoleon called us a nation of shopkeepers more than 100 years ago. More tea?"

David and I nod in gratitude.

"I . . ."

"Yes, Mrs Coulthurst?"

"I was wondering why you wanted us to attend the bank in person."

The fact that no one specifically invited my own presence is not lost on the manager, whose countenance betrays this truth.

"Ah yes," he answers, having digested his last gulp of beverage, "I'll come straight to the point – in two words, Mill Farm."

"Mill Farm?" queries David. "What have we to do with Mill Farm?"

"You know it's vacant and up for sale?"

"Yes."

I feel bound to interrupt: "It wasn't very nice what you did to the Patemans."

"No, Mrs Coulthurst, it wasn't, but it was necessary. You will understand, of course, that I cannot break any confidences. Suffice it to say, however, the decision to foreclose was taken at a higher level and I had no real say in the matter."

So Mr Lamacraft has received absolution, at least in his own mind.

"Frankly, Mr Coulthurst," he continues, "I'm rather surprised you haven't expressed an interest in Mill Farm yourself, given that it adjoins your own property."

David looks at him askance.

"Mr Lamacraft, my wife and I shall not finish paying for Vine's Farm until 1944. That's another sixteen years. How could we possibly contemplate taking on another holding at this time?"

"Come, come, Mr Coulthurst – you are too modest. The successful businessman, as well as adapting to changing conditions, needs to focus on the benefits of expansion. He may thereby accrue the advantages of economy of scale. By spreading his fixed assets over a larger acreage a farmer has scope to increase his profits."

"Or increase his losses during an agricultural depression," David counters cynically.

"But not you, Mr Coulthurst. You are swimming against the tide of failure."

Neither David nor I am convinced by the manager's thesis.

"When a man expands on borrowed money," David explains, "the one thing he's bound to increase is his liability. You must know that any additional land we might acquire would have to be purchased on mortgage."

Lamacraft looks uncharacteristically sanguine.

"But of course," he concedes, "and that's where the bank comes in."

I feel compelled to intercede: "Mr Lamacraft, my husband and I work very hard to keep our heads above water. I should be less than honest with you if I didn't point out that running a farm efficiently seems to require a never-ending investment in machinery. We've had to buy a tractor, a plough to fit the tractor, a milking machine, an engine to power the milking machine, bottling machinery, two motor vans . . ."

I note that, rather than throwing his hands high in despair, the manager appears almost euphoric at my list of seemingly profligate expenditure.

He cannot resist interrupting me: "All this," he enthuses, "and still you deny yourselves the comforts of electricity and sanitation. You put your business above self-indulgence. What pioneers you are! Don't you see now how your investments have paid off? You're farming for the present and future whilst most farmers are living in the past and going to the wall. Not for you the horse and cart and milking cows by hand with nothing more than a bucket. No, indeed, you are farming for the twentieth century, not the nineteenth!"

David and I are almost exhausted.

"As you say," I reply, "we haven't got electricity or sanitation yet, so we're hardly that modern."

"But you will," Lamacraft retorts. "You're waiting for the national grid to arrive, I expect. Then you can have hot water on tap and put in a bathroom too."

"Well," David interjects, "we're certainly not going to spend money on a generator."

"Of course you're not," the manager confirms almost gleefully. "You see, you really are a successful businessman. An impatient fool would buy a generator which produces expensive electricity and then discard his purchase once the grid becomes available. You, on the other hand, know the right moment to strike. You save the money you might have spent on a generator or put the cash to better use on the farm."

"Well, that's obvious," my husband returns somewhat disdainfully.

"I'm glad you agree, Mr Coulthurst. Now let me put my cards on the table. The bank is not a farmer and we are stuck with a farm we cannot sell in the present climate. It ought to sell because now is a good time for someone to enter the market at a depressed price, but there it is. A farm needs a good farmer to make it profitable. The fact is that Mill Farm is a liability to us. We deal in money, not land. We lent Mr Pateman money, and our loan has turned into soil, which stymies the bank rather than lets us go about our normal business. We need to free up this frozen asset by liquefying it, and that's where you come in."

"I think I've made it perfectly clear," David answers, "that we're in no position to take on a further mortgage. And, to be honest, I'm not sure expansion is a good idea for us anyway."

"Why not?"

"Because any enterprise has only a certain capacity. We've built up a milk and egg retail business which serves a limited local area. There's little scope to expand as further afield is well served by others. If we wished to deliver to a wider area, then we should have to take trade away from them to the detriment of their businesses. It would be like robbing Peter to pay Paul. We wouldn't be creating new wealth, only invading another's territory. I don't believe in a dog-eat-dog society."

Lamacraft bows his head towards his desk and wrings his hands in barely disguised frustration.

"Have you ever thought, Mr Coulthurst, that others would be quite willing to break your business in order to benefit their own?"

"They've already tried it," admits David, "and we've seen them off. There's now an uneasy truce. Let's be clear: there's no advantage in trying to destroy each other. To do that would spark a price war with financial returns diminishing to the point where only losses are incurred by everyone. Then it's survival of the fittest with winner taking all. The survivor would be the business with the largest reserves of capital – the one which could sustain losses for the longest period. That business would then control the price of its produce, which means the consumer paying over the odds so the winner could recoup its losses and make handsome profits thereafter. Thus everybody would lose, except the enterprise with the most muscle. Mr Lamacraft, I have to tell you now that Vine's Farm does not have the most muscle, and I am just content to enjoy my current market share and pay off our mortgage by the due date."

I breathe a sigh of relief that David has put our case so well, but the bank manager has not yet yielded.

"Mr Coulthurst, you don't sell all your milk and eggs retail, do you?"

"It's yes for the eggs and no for the milk."

"Indeed, so a proportion of your milk production is sold wholesale in churns, is it not?"

"Yes."

"And would I be right in thinking that even this is profitable?"

"Yes, but the margin is much smaller."

"Even so, if the profit is there, then there is scope for expansion; after all, even Mr Pateman had a market for his milk. It's not as though you would have to find a new outlet for any milk produced at Mill Farm."

David and I glance at each other a little wearisomely.

"Mill Farm wasn't just producing milk," David sighs at length. "It was a mixed enterprise, producing everything under the sun."

"Exactly!" returns Lamacraft, as though he has trumped a high card laid down by my husband. "There were too many activities which lost money. Specialising in one or two profitable areas, as you have done, is the formula for success."

I decide that I must intervene, if for no other reason than that David might become irritable and suffer pain in his wounded leg, through which he would become even more irritable.

"Mr Lamacraft, my husband has made it plain that we feel committed enough financially with our outstanding mortgage on Vine's Farm. It would be folly for us to increase our liabilities through a further loan. Personally, I find the prospect frightening. We have two children to support as well as my mother-in-law."

The bank manager begins to share our fatigue.

"Well, of course, if you don't feel up to taking on Mill Farm, then I suppose there's little more to be said."

"It's not just the land," David argues. "There's the house, cottages and farm buildings. What use would they be to us?"

The change in Lamacraft's countenance makes me wish David had remained silent.

"If you would take on the land and knock two farms into one, Mr Coulthurst, the bank could sell the dwellings and convert the other buildings to fulfil some different purpose."

"It's out of the question," I interject quickly. "I'm sorry, but that's it and all about it."

The manager frowns, but seems determined to pursue matters further.

"It is possible, Mrs Coulthurst, that you and your husband could help the bank and, in so doing, benefit yourselves in the short term."

"How so?" David enquires.

"By renting the land while we continue seeking a purchaser. We are currently keeping on two of Mr Pateman's former employees to prevent the holding from deteriorating, but the place is not really being farmed as such. What this property needs is someone to run it properly whilst it is on the market. It would then look more attractive to a prospective buyer."

"To run it properly, as you put it," David replies, "would take financial investment over and above any rent you might charge. Farming investment is long-term. How could that benefit us when you might, at the drop of a hat, find a buyer and tell us we must therefore vacate forthwith?"

"Well, it wouldn't be so drastic as that, Mr Coulthurst. I don't doubt we could come to some amicable arrangement whereby both you and the bank are advantaged. Now look – you and your wife would probably like time to think about all this. Next week I shall be hosting one of our business luncheons here at the bank. I would like to invite you both cordially to attend. You would meet some interesting people. Won't you come?"

Mr Lamacraft has softened our resolve and appealed to our curiosity. No wonder business lunches are considered such a potent weapon in the pursuit of commerce. Anyway, what have we got to lose by not going save an appetising meal at someone else's expense?

CHAPTER 15

TEMPTATION AND AMBITION

In the ensuing days there is only one topic of adult conversation in our farmhouse. The bank manager has sown a seed which threatens to germinate into an unknown plant. Clara leaves David and me in no doubt that Mill Farm should be left to its own devices and that the luncheon invitation bodes ill – an opportunity to sweet-talk us into injudicious resolution.

Forewarned is forearmed, and David, too, casts a suspicious eye upon such hospitality given by lenders of capital.

"Don't expect the other guests to be the best of their credit customers," he advises me. "A bank makes little or nothing out of them. No, the people they court are those who borrow at interest with the ability to keep servicing a loan over years and decades. These borrowers think they are working for themselves, but in reality they are working for the bank and paying it for the privilege. All the bank does is sit back, watch these poor fools work themselves into the ground and then count the proceeds of their labour."

Clara nods sagely.

While not wishing to defend the banks, I feel an inclination to challenge my husband's cynical analysis.

"But, darling, surely you cannot deny that banks perform a useful service. How could industry function without capital being made available to create economic wealth for the nation?"

"You can tell", Clara informs her son, "that she was educated privately."

I blush slightly.

"I'm lucky to have such an intelligent wife," David asserts.

"I don't know that I'm really intelligent, but perhaps we should remember that we borrowed money to buy this farm."

"Because we were forced to," retorts Clara. "It was either that or be put out. Anyway, you've got a way with words, but don't let them cloud your judgment."

It is with this wise counsel that David and I set out for the bank on the appointed day. If I am a little apprehensive, then I feel positively intimidated when we arrive, for I am the only woman present. I am conscious of the fact that all eyes seem to be focused in my direction and I begin to wish I were back at Vine's Farm performing any rural chore no matter how demanding or unpleasant.

The situation is about to become much worse. Mr Lamacraft catches my attention.

"Ah, Mrs Coulthurst, I don't know how many of our guests you have met before, but there must be at least one."

He beckons me over to another gentleman.

"Now, Mrs Coulthurst, of course you know your own solicitor, Mr Stansfield."

I now wish the floor would open up beneath my feet and convey me to a place of privacy, free of embarrassment. If only I had possessed the sense to consult my father about this luncheon. I fear that once Mr Lamacraft learns of our relationship he will distrust the contents of my father's letter and, worse still, will abandon any trust he has in Poppa, David and me.

My father, however, is nothing if not quick-witted, and he has the presence of mind to rescue his daughter. Without a trace of guilt, he shakes my hand.

"Mrs Coulthurst, of course, how do you do? Your husband is well, I trust?"

I do hope my countenance does not betray me. In truth, I wish I could now hug my dear father and tell the assembled company what a wonderful man he is.

"Well, I must circulate," Lamacraft advises. "Please excuse me."

He departs, much to my relief.

"Thank you, Poppa," I whisper, in the manner of a wayward offspring. "Do you think he guessed?"

"Who? Old Lamacraft? No, he's too full of himself at present, but what on earth are you and David doing here?"

I explain the situation to him.

"I know I should have asked your advice about all this," I confess.

I can sense my father's brain working as he pauses to absorb what I have related.

"Well, my dear, if you and David are in any way disposed towards taking on Mill Farm temporarily, then you should strike the severest of bargains. The bank wants you to do it a favour, and for that it should pay a stiff price."

I ask my father to elucidate.

"For a start they should make it available rent-free. Furthermore, any standing crops should be yours when you market them. You should then be allowed to sow what you like. I'm no farmer, but I think, in the current circumstances, you should grass the whole place over. Better still, let the fields tumble down to grass by natural regeneration. Grass is the natural plant of the English countryside. You can get it for free. Why spend good money on a farm which may only be in your possession for a few months?"

Prior to taking our seats for luncheon, I convey my father's observations to David.

"I suppose we could tell Lamacraft to take it or leave it," he muses in response.

As we consume a more than adequate meal there is copious business conversation reaching my ears from left, right and opposite. I try to assimilate as much as possible. Controlling costs, avoiding overmanning and pricing one's goods to the limit which the market will stand seem to be the most oft-repeated mantras. It is rammed down my throat that, unless one sells directly to the consumer, as we do with milk and eggs, then farming is an enterprise where the participant cannot price his own produce at all. We are told by our purchaser how much he will pay for a quarter of wheat. It is all about world markets and the law of supply and demand. A drought in one country may enhance agricultural returns in another; likewise a flood or war. When all seems well, and crops are plentiful, prices fall or even collapse.

When I raise my voice to a level audible to more than the two people nearest me, I am conscious of a marked drop in discourse elsewhere. I am also more than a little embarrassed that everyone now appears to be looking in my direction.

"You were saying, Mrs Coulthurst," our host remarks in encouragement.

"Well," I begin nervously, "farming is like very few other businesses."

"You mean primary producers?" enquires my father, still pretending that I am not his daughter.

"Er, yes, Mr Stansfield, those of us at the end of a trade chain."

"And at the wrong end, to boot!" my father persists.

"Yes, quite; you see, we cannot set our prices to the limit of the market."

"Unless you form a cartel, like the oil producers," claims Poppa, whose interventions I like to think are designed to support my argument rather than to unnerve me.

"You make an important point, Mr Stansfield," chimes in David. "Oil producers can agree to limit supply or flood the market as the mood takes them, but there are too many farmers throughout the world to agree on anything."

"Quite right, Mr Coulthurst," my father responds. "They also produce such a diverse range of foodstuffs. To get the world farming community to form a cartel is totally impracticable."

"I doubt any government would countenance it," David asserts. "Food shortages have sparked revolutions. Look what happened in Russia and Germany."

"Gentlemen, gentlemen," interjects Lamacraft, "you are forgetting Mrs Coulthurst. She was about to make a point."

My husband and father feign being the objects of admonishment and smile benignly at me.

124

"I rather think Mr Stansfield and my husband have made my point for me. I was only going to add that farmers cannot set their prices at all unless they sell directly to the public, which is hardly possible with commodities such as cereals. I mean, you can scarcely sell a bushel of wheat to a housewife and tell her to make her own bread with it!"

My intervention is met with gales of laughter. I resolve to expand my thesis.

"Is anyone here a grocer, a greengrocer, a baker or a butcher?"

A few hands are raised sheepishly.

"Suppose I came into one of your shops, selected items and then told you how much I was going to pay for them?"

"I'd advise you to think again: pay the proper price or leave the goods with me," answers one man.

"If you persisted, madam, I think I'd summon a constable," responds another.

"Exactly!" I exclaim. "You'd consider me to be a preposterous woman – a troublemaker who should be removed at once. Yet that is the way farmers are treated. No matter how hard we work, or how good the quality of our produce, wholesale customers tell us how much they are going to pay for our efforts. If the price they quote is below the cost of production, then we have an unenviable choice: take it or leave it. That is, make a loss or fail to market our wares. Not a very good way to do business, is it?"

There follows a general murmuring, broken only by a man who is decidedly unsympathetic to my cause.

"Farmers are the landowning class," he asserts. "They look down on us who're in trade. They can take a bad year now and again. They never mention the good years."

I feel my blood beginning to boil.

"Since the repeal of the Corn Production Act there haven't been any good years!" I retort. "And not all farmers are landowners. Most of them are tenants. Even many of those who are owner-occupiers are saddled with a mortgage which has to be serviced in near-impossible trading conditions."

"Mrs Coulthurst is quite right," interjects Mr Lamacraft. "We are the mortgagees of the farm run by her and her husband. May I just say that my bank is the proud mortgagee of such an enterprising couple. Notwithstanding the many difficulties faced by agriculture today, Mr and Mrs Coulthurst are taking a leaf out of your book, gentlemen, through marketing some of their produce directly to the housewife."

"And trying to put the rest of us out of business, I suppose," returns one cynic.

"Not at all," avers Lamacraft. "You don't have cows and chickens to look after. You just wait for someone to deliver goods to your shop. Mr and Mrs Coulthurst increase the profit on their milk and eggs through selling them door to door, thereby cutting out the middleman."

My father, sitting almost opposite me, has a twinkle in his eye.

"By Jove, Lamacraft," he remarks, "you've put your finger on it. The stuff of a businessman or businesswoman is measured by how he or she adapts to market forces. It's no good moaning and groaning when there exists scope to succeed where many may be failing."

"Just so, Mr Stansfield. Let every man and, er, woman stand up for their own enterprise without trying to denigrate others; and let every business consider the merits of expansion, thus taking its success to new heights."

Lamacraft is looking at both David and me now, no doubt making a tacit reference to Mill Farm. It comes as no surprise therefore that once lunch is over he invites us to join him in his office.

"I'll come straight to the point," he says sharply: "Mill Farm – surely we can help each other out here?"

David explains with an unintended pun that the agricultural holding in question could be something of a millstone around our necks. He stresses the success of our current enterprise as being predicated on its restricted size. Twice the acreage and twice the number of cows (if we can afford them, which we cannot) do not guarantee twice the number of domestic customers for our milk; and the same principle applies to egg production.

David explains further that, given the traditional investment, Mill Farm is likely to make us a loss, as it did for the Patemans. There is only one way it could turn a profit – or more likely, break even – and that would be for us to farm it rent-free until it is sold.

Mr Lamacraft looks aghast.

"Rent-free!" he protests. "But everything has a value."

"Consider this," my husband answers: "You want to sell Mill Farm as soon as possible, but know this will be difficult in the present economic climate. Your main concern now is that the farm does not become derelict and less attractive to a prospective purchaser than it already is. So you want it to be kept neat and tidy – in short, farmed. You wish to do this at minimum, or preferably zero, cost. Currently you are employing two labourers, but they can't actually farm the property. They're just ensuring it doesn't go to rack and ruin. Am I right?"

Lamacraft nods his head in resignation.

"Very well," David continues, "here is what we propose: you let us rent the farm for a peppercorn rent and give us a minimum of three months' notice to quit. At the time of quitting you pay us the value of any growing crops or allow us to harvest them in due season. In return we'll farm the land in a workmanlike manner and maintain all hedges and ditches. We don't need the house, so you can rent it out as you wish. I'm afraid it's a matter of take it or leave it."

The bank manager sighs heavily, as though he has nothing left with which to bargain.

"You realise, of course, Mr Coulthurst, that any final decision in this matter does not rest with me. I don't know what my superiors will say. I'll make what representations I can on your behalf, although I'm disappointed you cannot see your way to offering some kind of reasonable rent."

"Like you, Mr Lamacraft, my hands are tied – not by having to answer to anyone else, but by financial reality. We are in the depths of agricultural depression and no politician seems disposed to do anything about it."

We take our leave and resolve not to think any more about the matter. Vine's Farm is our enterprise, and its neighbour is nothing to do with us unless the bank makes it so. Our only concession to this policy is to relate the day's events to Clara, who grunts her disapproval of any notion that we should farm beyond the confines of our present holding.

Weeks pass and David begins to grow impatient that we have heard nothing further about Mill Farm. It is not that he is eager to learn anything purely for its own sake, but June is rapidly approaching and grass on the unoccupied property will soon need mowing for hay.

"The best hay is made in June, when the plants are beginning to flower," he informs me anxiously. "I know what's going on: the bank's delaying a decision, hoping I'll weaken first. Then they'll try and get a rent out of us. What's the betting they'll wait until the corn needs cutting in August, or even September? Just like a bank to put pressure on the little man!"

"I think you're taking a cynical view, darling," I tell him. "A bank has many decisions to make, not just about Mill Farm."

I do not appear to have placated him as he paces around the farmhouse kitchen as ably as his wounded leg permits.

"Look," I continue, "if you're that worried, tell the bank every crop will suffer unless they hurry up and come to an agreement."

"Yes, that's exactly what they'd like so they can hold us to ransom."

"Then give them an ultimatum: if they haven't decided by the end of next week, then the whole deal is off!"

David looks shocked at my suggestion. It is almost as though he has become inured to the idea that we should be quite large farmers through doubling our acreage, even temporarily. I do hope he is not becoming too ambitious.

The tension in our home grows with every day until the fateful letter arrives. David tears open the envelope with a zeal usually reserved for children emptying their Christmas stockings. I try to be patient as he digests its contents.

"They've agreed to our terms!" he exclaims excitedly.

Clara and I are at pains to bring him back to earth.

"I hope you know what you're doing, boy," his mother grumbles. "There's many a man in the bankruptcy court who got too big for his boots!"

As David comes to terms with the task ahead, so I detect a chill of uncertainty coursing through his veins.

"Well, darling," I remark, "a greater deal of responsibility has now fallen upon our shoulders and we shall have to discharge it."

CHAPTER 16

MILL FARM

Our initial task at Mill Farm is to secure the hay crop in good condition. We retain the services of the two labourers employed by the bank, and now we are responsible for their wages, which places an immediate burden on our budget.

These men, both in their fifties, are mightily relieved not to be made redundant; but they have grown up with the horse and seem scarcely adaptable to a more mechanised approach to agriculture. They view our solitary power unit in the form of Beatrice, the tractor, with no small degree of suspicion.

Demands upon Beatrice will be severely increased with a larger acreage, but a second tractor is quite beyond our financial reach. So we embark upon haymaking on both farms, and we are soon aware of the enormity of the job in comparison with previous years. As the buildings at Mill Farm are empty, David decides to stack hay unthatched in one of the barns. The roof obviates the need for thatching and thus saves time. The two Mill Farm labourers are astonished at this behaviour, and opine that something must be wrong with such an innovation. David tells them that rain is less likely to penetrate clay tiles than it would thatch.

Notwithstanding our policy, many local farming sages stop to observe the unthatched shallow hayricks in the barn. It seems to them as though centuries of agricultural practice have been consigned to the dustbin. With Beatrice chugging in fields instead of plodding shires nodding their heads in apparent approval, it seems the rural community believes David and I have taken leave of our senses.

It is predictably a much longer haymaking, extending well into

July. The traditional welcome interval between this task and the corn harvest is almost cut to nothing before we set the binder to reap the oats and barley which John Pateman sowed last autumn. It is a relief that our harvest at Vine's Farm is so small: just one field of winter barley to feed our beef cattle. In contrast, the Patemans sowed nearly eighty acres of oats, barley and wheat, which are going to keep us busy for some weeks.

"Be you going to stack corn in barn without thatch, guv'nor?" enquires one of the Mill Farm workers.

"Certainly," answers David, "if there's enough room."

The other shakes his head in disbelief.

It comes to pass, however, that every open-fronted building, no matter how low its roof, is crammed full of sheaves waiting to be threshed during autumn.

It is when the harvest is completed in late September that serious decision-making is necessary at Mill Farm. There is no telling when we shall be given notice to quit this holding, so we are reluctant to invest for the coming farming year despite any compensation which the bank may pay us.

David and I consider my father's suggestion that we should let the corn stubbles tumble down to grass at zero cost. My father is no farmer, but he numbers several amongst his clients, and many have adopted such a policy as returns on cereals continue to fall.

When the Patemans left Mill Farm, dung in the cattle's winter quarters had not been removed to form a midden outside. This substance has remained in situ ever since. David lays great store on farmyard manure and he seizes the opportunity to convey this consignment for the benefit of our own holding. He calculates that dung from both farms will be sufficient to apply a heavy dressing to the field destined for our small crop of barley.

Clearing rotting straw soaked with bovine droppings is back-breaking work performed with hand forks. Each fork-load is weighty and has to be heaved on to a tip-cart for transportation to the land. So distasteful is this task that it tends to be accompanied by language which a lady should not hear, so I make myself scarce.

We resolve not to spend any of our meagre resources on the

arable fields at Mill Farm, but to let them regenerate naturally. This is a polite term for abandoning them to their fate during autumn and winter before waiting to see what spring will bring. The hope is that useful grassland may emerge. I am reminded of my father's observation that grass is the natural plant of the countryside, yet David advises me that we can also expect to be greeted by broad-leaved weeds such as docks and thistles, which will need to be removed by hand. Volunteer cereals, from grain accidentally shaken out when moving sheaves at harvest time, will inevitably be present, but they can easily be grazed or cut when still green to be included in a hay crop. All this is untidy farming, but it is sympathetic to our pocket.

In an attempt to realise the quickest financial return from our labours at Mill Farm, we offer hay for sale and beg the threshing contractor to pay us a visit at his earliest convenience. No one seems to want the hay because so much land in our district has already been grassed down. The only way that we can use it to advantage is to increase our dairy herd, and this is expensive. To defray such a cost we need to sell grain from the Mill Farm harvest. Thus we are stymied until late November, when traction engine and threshing machine at last rumble into the farmyard.

The miserable price of corn is such that there is precious little margin for an arable farmer. David and I, however, do have an advantage, if only for the 1928 harvest. We have secured the Mill Farm cereals for nothing save the costs of harvesting and threshing. Therefore, even in these straitened times, we are able to turn an arable profit, which gives us scope to purchase some in-calf heifers. A sobering thought: I am reminded of the parable of the talents in that we have reaped what we have not sown.

Now would be an excellent time for us to quit Mill Farm. It has given us all that we could expect to make out of it. When the holding first came to market a large wooden board was erected by the estate agent charged with selling the property on behalf of the bank. The board was brightly painted so as to attract the attention of prospective buyers passing along the road. The agent would no doubt claim that much interest has been shown in acquiring this sought-after holding. It is true that several people did come to view it, perhaps more out of curiosity than serious intent. The number of viewings began to decline to a trickle and now seems to have ceased all together. The wooden board is still there, but the paint has faded somewhat in unison with the interest.

David has instructed the two labourers we have inherited to cut hedges and clear ditches in compliance with our duty to the bank. This is hard, unpleasant handwork, often undertaken in the rain and cold. It is also frustrating for us in that we are paying for this labour, which yields no financial return. Mill Farm is beginning to cost us money.

There is a little economic respite, however, now that threshing is completed. A few local farmers have expressed interest in purchasing some of our straw. Having grassed their holdings, they need to acquire this commodity for bedding down their cattle during winter. A few valuable pounds are raised in this way, yet it hardly provides a significant contribution to the farm balance sheet.

1929 opens its account with the usual frost and later some snow. It is now that we receive a slightly more substantial monetary boost. The cold weather results in livestock consuming more hay, and a neighbour asks whether he may purchase some of our surplus supply. David, in rather mischievous form, says that despite the huge demand he can let his colleague have what he wants at a price which gives us cause for cheer. Pursuant to predictable grumbling, the man pays up and agrees to transport the feed himself. I can only hope this presages a happy new year.

As spring breaks cover I have reason to be even more optimistic – ecstatic, in fact. I receive a letter from Dotty, my old school friend. She is getting married – no, wait, she is married! I can hardly believe it – not that I think Dotty could only be unbecoming to a man, but there is such a shortage of men for women of our age and at twenty-nine Dotty would certainly be regarded by most as an old maid. All this does seem rather sudden.

Should I feel slighted? I chose Dotty as my maid of honour when I married David. Perhaps I should not be selfish. Dotty has lived in London for several years now and must have made many new friends whom she sees more frequently than me. She wants to visit us and bring her new husband. I am so excited and tell David, who is equally delighted and pleased for us to extend an invitation to spend a few days at Vine's Farm.

When I write to ask whether Mr and Mrs Henry Claxton would like to be met at our local railway station, Dotty informs me that they will be motoring down from the metropolis. So they have a motor car, and therefore it appears that the mysterious Henry is a man of substance. Perhaps Dotty has really fallen on her feet.

On the appointed day they are set to arrive in time for lunch. I find myself eagerly popping out from the kitchen to peer through one of the front windows to see if a strange vehicle is approaching. Clara and I are preparing the meal while my four-and-a-half-year-old daughter, Becky, is trying to help. My son, James, is at school. David is changing from his working clothes into something more presentable. He descends the staircase and tells me to stop fussing. He will answer the door at the appropriate moment.

"I hope they'll not be late," grumbles Clara, glancing at the kitchen clock. "The food will spoil otherwise."

"Have they got children, Mummy?" enquires Becky in hopeful expectation of finding a playmate.

I smile as I tell her that I do not think they have had time for such things!

It is now David who is peering out of a front window.

"They're here!" he exclaims excitedly. "And what a car!"

I rush to join him.

"It's rather big," I observe.

"It's a Wolseley 21/60," my husband explains: "a straight eight engine with an overhead camshaft."

"Well, that's over my head, darling. What a long bonnet!"

"It's a long engine," David enthuses. "Eight cylinders: just the job for a long journey."

So, a long bonnet for a long engine for a long journey – I just hope Dotty has a long marriage. Brushing my husband aside, I open the front door. Dotty and I embrace in mutual euphoria. She holds out her hand to reveal her obviously expensive wedding ring. It has the biggest diamond I have ever seen.

"This is Henry," she announces.

I try not to look shocked or surprised. Her husband is an elegant, well-attired gentleman with impeccable manners, yet it cannot be any exaggeration to say that he is old enough to be Dotty's father. I find myself thinking, 'Long bonnet, long engine, long journey, long in the tooth.' Silently I admonish myself. Who am I to pass judgment on what might be Dotty's only chance of happiness?

At lunch it transpires that Henry was Dotty's employer before they married.

"I lost my wife eighteen months ago," he explains. "I don't mind telling you, I became terribly lonely. I saw this lovely lady in my office day after day, and I thought, 'Why not?' So I asked her out, and I'm delighted to say love blossomed. I feel a very lucky man."

"We're so pleased," I respond.

"I really thought my chance had gone," admits Dotty.

"Have you got any children, Henry?" David enquires.

"Yes, three boys, all too young to have fought in the war, thank God."

"But they're nearly as old as I am," jokes Dotty.

"Have they accepted you?" I ask with an impudence which I regret instantly.

"Oh yes, they think it's all rather fun, don't they, Henry?"

"Indeed, I'd say they're even jealous that a man of my age can still attract a young woman."

"I've actually become a step-grandmother whilst still in my twenties," bubbles Dotty.

"My eldest son has a baby daughter," Henry explains.

"Oo," interjects Becky, "I wish I could see her."

"Well, young lady, perhaps one day you will."

During the afternoon Dotty and I take a stroll in the garden.

"I know what you're going to say, Vera."

"What?"

"Oh, come on – that he's old enough to be my father."

"I wasn't going to say any such thing."

"But you're thinking it."

"Look, Dotty – I'm just glad you've found someone you can be happy with. I'd say the same if he were ninety."

"Well, he's only fifty-four."

"There you are, then. Have you heard from Lilian?"

"Yes, and would you believe she's coming down to Honeysuckle Cottage tomorrow?"

"I didn't know. She's been so busy working that she hasn't visited her country retreat for ages."

"She's preparing for her first talking picture."

"That's going to be a challenge."

"Thing is, Vera, the film companies are keen to engage stage-trained actors and actresses. It's the voice, you see. Some of the silent stars can't speak properly and haven't had experience of learning lines. It's a whole new discipline for the cinema now."

"Well, Lilian won't have any problem. She's perfect at everything: acting, singing, miming . . ."

"Yes, we all knew she'd succeed when we were at school. Do you remember when she sang for those wounded soldiers down here and you played the piano?"

I cast my mind back more than a decade.

Of course I do. It seems like another world though now, doesn't it?"

The better of our two milk vans returns James from his school. Dotty enquires whether we still have 'that funny old pre-war Model T'.

"Yes, Lizzy's getting very old, but we can't afford to replace her yet."

We all take afternoon tea in the parlour. James and Becky pass round sandwiches and cakes.

"Want to buy a farm?" David asks Henry.

Dotty looks horrified.

"You're not going to sell this place and give up farming?"

"Absolutely not!" David and I chorus.

"Then I don't understand," adds Dotty.

We explain the matter of Mill Farm and its failure to find a purchaser.

"It's early days yet," opines Henry. "It's not like selling a car or even a house."

"Wouldn't you be interested in having a place in the country rather like Lilian?" I enquire.

"We already have one," Henry announces. "An ample dwelling set in its own grounds, albeit in Surrey, and I hardly think Lilian's cottage can compare with a farm of 150 acres."

It is clear that Henry's interest in agriculture only extends to curiosity and he lets it be known that he is fully aware our industry has been in depression for several years.

"And I concede it's getting worse for you," he sighs. "People want cheap food and they don't much care where it comes from. World markets dictate the price of your produce. Your returns only seem to perk up when there's a disaster somewhere or other, like drought, flood or war. Create a shortage of anything, then the man with a warehouse full of it is king."

Henry undoubtedly has a wise business head on his shoulders, which is why he would not contemplate a farming investment in current circumstances.

"I'll tell you one thing," he asserts whilst accepting an iced cake from Becky: "all falling markets bottom out eventually; and when they do, that is the time to strike. The skill is trying to predict the bottom and then investing before everyone climbs in and sends prices through the roof."

"I wish we'd bought Vine's Farm at the bottom of the market instead of the top," David laments. "But then, it only became available at the wrong time."

Henry finishes his mouthful of cake before replying: "You may have an opportunity coming your way," he surmises. "If you can sense when things are likely to turn for the better, you might be able to buy Mill Farm yourself for a pittance and ultimately reap the rewards. A man with 300 acres is in a better position than one with half that area when profits are to be made. It's the economy of scale."

"You sound like our bank manager," I tell Henry. "He tried to get us to buy Mill Farm and rack up a debt we couldn't possibly service."

"Oh, you were right not to do that, my dear. The time is not yet opportune, but it may be one day."

CHAPTER 17

A CHILL WIND FROM ABROAD

On the morrow another powerful car pulls into Vine's Farm. I can see immediately it is the Lagonda in which Lilian, Dotty and I journeyed to our school reunion at Endacott nearly two years ago. From the driving seat out steps Lilian looking like a million pounds. There is nothing in my wardrobe to compare with her outfit save for a pair of silk stockings which rarely have I cause to wear. Even little Becky stands agog at this feminine apparition of perfection coming towards us.

"Mummy, that's what I want to look like when I'm grown-up."

I tell her that she is in for a long wait.

James, aged seven and a half, is more interested in the car. Henry kindly showed him his sedate-looking Wolseley yesterday, but Lilian's rather sporty vehicle with its fold-down roof seems a far more intriguing prospect.

Lilian, in her ever present theatrical manner, holds out her arms to greet us.

"Darling Vera," she begins, "and David, my, how you little ones have grown! It's been too long. You must think I've abandoned you all."

"Not a bit of it," I reply, and I confess that I was not expecting her to call despite being told she was to visit her cottage.

"Oh, I wouldn't dream of not seeing you first," purrs Lilian. "And how are the newly weds?"

"You'd better come in and meet them."

Lilian stays for lunch and regales us with humorous stories about her show-business career. It all seems 1,000 miles away from rustic life in the Sussex countryside.

David tries his "Do you want to buy a farm?" routine with our latest guest, and Lilian humours him as though she is onstage playing to a packed house.

"Oh, David, could you imagine it? I mean, what would it do to my fingernails? And then there's all those – how shall put it? – rural smells. Of course it would all be fun for a few minutes, but my idea of odour only extends to perfume, not to what comes out of a cow's rear end! I could play the role of a farmer's wife onstage or on a film set for as long as a director might wish, but that's what I am: just a humble actress. I merely play at being things, not doing them for real."

"I take it that's a no?" sighs my husband.

"Oh, David, you're so funny. I thought you were funny when I first met you. He is funny, isn't he, Vera? Aren't you glad you married a man with a sense of humour?"

I smile, hopefully sweetly.

"How do you like Honeysuckle Cottage, Lilian?" enquires Dotty.

"It's absolutely divine, but, alas, still devoid of electricity. When do you suppose this new national grid will grace us with its presence?"

"They erected the first pylon near Edinburgh last year," Henry advises.

"Edinburgh!" exclaims Lilian. "Well, that's all right for our Caledonian cousins, but hardly any use for us in this neck of the woods."

"I understand the first part of the grid is due to open in Central Scotland next year," adds Henry.

"Well, that's still no good for us," Lilian complains. "I'm tired of lighting oil lamps every time I come down here; and having a bath is a major operation with this business of trying to heat enough water."

"These pylons," David remarks: "I suppose they'll have to cross farmland. It'll spoil the countryside, won't it?"

"Some of it, perhaps," Henry admits, "but I believe landowners will be compensated."

"How much?" asks David, thereby giving credibility to the urban myth that farmers are always grasping for money.

"I'm not sure, old man, but I believe one can either be paid so much per annum or take a single lump sum."

"What do you advise?"

"Difficult to say until we have the figures, but I often regard a bird in the hand to be worth two in the bush."

"One could have a generator," suggests Dotty.

"They're expensive to buy and to run," answers David lugubriously, "although I'm surprised you've never acquired one for Honeysuckle Cottage, Lilian. Besides, it'd be a waste of money now that mains power is not too far away."

We all resign ourselves to living in or visiting rural Sussex without electricity for a few more years.

Giving thought to planting potatoes in our kitchen garden, David suddenly has a brainwave. His plan is to grow them on a slightly larger scale at Mill Farm, whereby our two labourers there can be put to spring work with profit in mind.

After buying enough seed to cover one acre he sets about ploughing and harrowing a field in which oats had previously been grown. A cartload of dung from our beef cattle yard is then dumped in the centre of cultivations. All the work from now on is done by hand. A hole is dug and a dollop of dung put in the bottom followed by a seed potato before backfilling with soil. Two wheelbarrows – one for dung and the other for potatoes – speed up the process.

Our two labourers are not enamoured of this strategy and they tell my husband it is bound to fail. Their analysis is not accepted by David, who irritates them further by issuing instructions to keep the crop weed-free by hoeing as necessary.

Once the laborious job of planting is completed, we have a period of rain and warmth which my husband suggests is God's reward for his enterprise.

"Just what those spuds need," he enthuses.

If the Mill Farm workers think their duties are about to become lighter, then they are in for a disappointment.

"Thistles and docks are coming in the grassed-down fields,"

David announces. "You must root them out whilst the ground is soft."

The two men look horrified.

"Don't 'ee know the ole rhyme, guvnor?" protests one: "Cut a thistle in May, labour thrown away. Cut 'im in June, see 'im again soon. Cut 'im in July, and 'e'll surely die."

"I'm not asking you to cut them. If you pull them and expose the roots to the air, then they're done for."

"You can't pull a thistle with your bare hands, guvnor," claims the other man. "You'd have 'em full o' thorns."

"That's why I'm supplying you with these suitable gloves," answers David triumphantly.

"You can't pull a dock up by the root," counters the first man.

"Yes, you can," asserts my husband. "Watch."

He stoops and with gloved hands slowly extracts an offending dock from the soil, its long taproot fully withdrawn to the atmosphere.

The two men look on with dismay.

David explains that this task can be achieved when the ground is sufficiently moist.

"You grip the weed with both hands and pull it gradually so it doesn't break off. The rest is mind over matter. If you believe it can come out completely, then it will."

Both labourers are concerned that the long grass will get their trousers wet.

"I see you're wearing hobnailed boots and gaiters," David observes. "You should buy some of those new gumboots."

"We'd still get our trousers wet, guvnor."

"Not if you tie some old sacks round your waists."

The men now seem to have exhausted their excuses, and they become resigned to the task laid before them.

"That job and the spud hoeing should keep them busy until haymaking," David informs me with a twinkle in his eye.

The potato growing has a double-edged benefit. As well as keeping the two men occupied, there will be scope to sell the crop to our milk and egg customers on the doorstep. Potatoes are heavy and cumbersome items for the housewife to carry, and we can undercut the greengrocers' prices. Our Mill Farm workers will have to dig the crop by hand, but they can do so at intervals according to customer demand.

For the moment, however, there is something else which takes precedence in my mind. A general election is approaching. Polling day is set for 30 May. It is the most significant election in my life inasmuch as it is the first at which I am entitled to vote. Every woman who has reached her twenty-first birthday may now enter the polling booth and place a cross in the box of her choice. It only irks me that I have had to wait so long. I celebrated my twenty-ninth birthday on 3 April. Were I but one year older I should have qualified to vote anyway under the franchise which has existed since 1918. I resolve to march into that polling station with all the determination shown by Clara eleven years ago.

On the appointed day my mother-in-law and I, with Becky in tow, stroll down to the village hall, where local voting is taking place. There is so much animated political conversation between Clara and me that my daughter becomes imbued with the notion that all three of us are entitled to vote. She considers it manifestly unfair that she remains disenfranchised. I explain that she will have to wait far less time than I had to, and several decades fewer than her grandmother.

The Conservative Prime Minister, Stanley Baldwin, has run his party's campaign under the slogans 'Safety First' and 'You Can Trust Me'. There is a school of thought, no doubt shared by Mr Baldwin and his colleagues, that the government's record is one which should not give rise to a change of administration. I tend to share this opinion, probably because of my upbringing, although I am painfully aware that nothing has been done to arrest the current decline in British agriculture. So I stare at my ballot paper, pausing to congratulate myself on a newly won entitlement, and with a flourish deposit a large black cross in the box adjacent to the name of our sitting Conservative Member of Parliament. He has served the community well and spoken up for farmers, albeit to no avail. I feel disinclined to punish a man who has tried to better our lot even though he has failed.

I emerge from the polling station with a grinning countenance as though I have just received a distinction in some school examination. Clara and Becky look at me as they would if I had undergone a childlike transformation. When my four-and-a-half-year-old daughter fixes me with a sympathetic stare, I know instantly that I am being at least a shade silly.

My debut in the polling booth has mixed results. Our local Conservative candidate is returned to Parliament, but Mr Baldwin's 'Safety First' campaign finishes in second place. Indeed, no political party wins an overall majority. We now have a hung Parliament in which the Labour Party has the largest number of seats. The King sends for Ramsay MacDonald, who advises His Majesty that he is able to form a minority government. I lack confidence that Mr MacDonald will have any more compassion for farmers than his predecessor, yet there is one bright spot. Margaret Bondfield, the ex-Brighton shop girl who did so much to advance the cause for trade-union representation and equal pay for women employed in retailing, has become the first female Cabinet minister. She is the new Minister of Labour – bully for her!

We begin to dig our potatoes in early July. The pessimism displayed by our two Mill Farm workers has proved unjustified. The crop is more than satisfactory, and the new potatoes are delicious. More importantly, we are taking liberal orders from our milk and egg customers. Both delivery vans now carry a large sack of potatoes and a small set of scales for weighing out the quantities purchased. Our bank manager, Mr Lamacraft, would be proud of us!

It is now more than a year since we took over Mill Farm, and the property still has not found a buyer. The farmhouse has been let to a recently retired schoolmaster and his wife, a Mr and Mrs Pilkington. They are most pleasant neighbours who seem keen to learn about farming, but they lack both the funds and youth to take up the calling. Mr Pilkington was a housemaster at a boys' public school – a post which provided accommodation for both him and his wife. Retirement therefore necessitated the search for a new home.

Mrs Pilkington has an aged mother resident in her own Kentish bungalow, which will be passed on to her only daughter in due course. The Pilkingtons are worried that Mill Farm will be sold before the bungalow is inherited, not least because the old lady is clinging fiercely on to life and values her independence. David and I counter by remarking that the bank is clinging fiercely on to ownership of the farm and therefore they may not need to move again before benefitting from the legacy.

My daughter, Becky, will be five in September, and the subject of her education has become a cause for concern. There is no way my husband and I can afford to pay school fees, but this problem is solved by my father making the necessary provision, as he did for our son, James. The sticking point is the fact that Becky is set upon attending my alma mater, Endacott College.

The school has now established its junior department, thus bringing to fruition Miss Buckmaster's ambition to take a girl aged five and guide her through to within three years of her majority. If Endacott were nearby, then there would not be an issue. Unfortunately it is some twenty miles distant and, although the train service is convenient, there are obvious difficulties. A five-year-old child cannot be expected to travel alone; neither can she be expected to board. Indeed, boarding facilities are not offered until the age of eight, and I consider even this to be inordinately young.

I have explained all this to Becky, but I am met repeatedly with the following response: "I want to go to Endacott."

This impasse has to be resolved, and I am almost at my wits' end. Whenever I find circumstances are defeating me on any matter, I have recourse to my father, without whom I sometimes feel life would be impossible. I say this without casting any aspersions on David, who also tends to adhere to the proposition that Charles Stansfield is a solver of insuperable problems.

"I'll drive her there and back."

"But, Poppa, that's forty miles per day. How can you afford the time?"

"I'm going to semi-retire. I shall retain a few of my oldest clients and pass the remaining work on to a young solicitor whom my partners and I are engaging."

"But your Austin Seven won't last long with all that mileage."

"Well, my dear, I'm going to trade in the old bus for something larger and more comfortable."

"But it's five days a week."

"Your mother and I shall enjoy the drive, and we'll have lunch somewhere nice."

"But you'll both get bored with the same old journey there and back day after day."

"It's only during term time. We'll have weekends and holidays to do other things."

I have exhausted all my *but*s, so one lucky little girl, upon whom her grandfather dotes, will come to attend the school of her choice – and she had better do justice to it.

Our farming year draws to its close at the end of September. We are left with the Mill Farm buildings stuffed with indifferent hay from naturally generated grassland. Unless we have a harsh winter I cannot see there being much of a market for all this bulk feed. If we hang on to this unwanted holding much longer, I can visualise our having more haystacks than anyone else in Sussex. Despite increasing the dairy herd at Vine's Farm, we know our cattle could not possibly eat everything produced next door.

Within a month something occurs of such ominous magnitude that our farming worries pale into insignificance. On 24 October the American stock market collapses. There has been such a transatlantic frenzy of purchasing shares in recent years that a bubble has expanded to the point where it has now burst. What has made the situation worse is that some people have actually been borrowing money to buy shares in the naive belief that their values will continue to increase indefinitely. The Wall Street Crash, as it has become known, has resulted in these persons being unable to repay their loans. In consequence, depositors are trying to recover their savings for fear that the banks may become insolvent.

My father tells me that when the United States sneezes the rest of the world catches a cold. Quite how this virus will spread in our country is uncertain, but events across the ocean do not bode well for us. Poppa goes on to say that there has been no run on a British bank since 1866, when Overend Gurney closed its doors in the wake of railway speculation.

"But we haven't been acting irresponsibly over here, have we?" I enquire nervously.

My father looks thoughtfully at me.

"No, my dear, but even if we have behaved well, an economic depression in America will probably translate into one everywhere else. Our banks may survive intact, yet business activity will decline. This may have devastating consequences for anyone without money. Cash will become king. Do you realise that Americans have been purchasing shares on the margin? That is, they buy in the expectation that the share price will rise significantly before settlement day. If it does, they sell at a profit and fulfil their obligations. If they make a loss and don't have money to defray the difference, then they're in trouble. If too many people are in trouble, then the whole system falls apart. When a quoted company becomes overvalued for too long its share price is bound to drop."

I try to digest what my ever wise father has told me.

"So, Poppa, if people cannot fulfil their obligations, they will become insolvent; and if they cannot repay any bank loans, there may be a run on the banks and depositors may be unable to recover their money and the banks will fold. An even larger number of people will then have less money to buy goods and services, so other people cannot make a living. Everything has a knock-on effect throughout the population, except for the few who have plenty of money."

"You seem to have grasped it, my dear. If businesses cannot find customers, then they must contract and lay off staff. The result will be mass unemployment and misery. I don't want to be a prophet of doom, but I fear we must all brace ourselves for a severe economic downturn. But you in farming have had several years of this already. Now the whole country may be plunged into depression. Let us be thankful that some of us will be better prepared than others to weather the storm."

CHAPTER 18

SLUMP

My father's analysis of how the Wall Street Crash might impact upon Britain proves dramatically accurate. Our volume of exports plummet and unemployment rises drastically.

The Labour government has been blaming the capitalist system for our economic woes, yet its own members are tearing themselves apart in searching for a solution. Lord Passfield is bereft of ideas. George Lansbury proposes lowering the retirement age to sixty to ease unemployment figures. Oswald Mosley advances radical policies of planned foreign trade, public direction of industry and a credit system to promote expansion. All this is too much for the Lord Privy Seal, J. H. Thomas, who relinquishes his task of combating unemployment and resurfaces as Dominions Secretary. Mosley's ideas are also an anathema to Philip Snowden, the Chancellor of the Exchequer, who rigidly adheres to the concept of free trade. Outside the government Ernest Bevin, General Secretary of the National Transport and General Workers' Union, suggests devaluation of our currency.

Snowden's 1930 budget lifts income tax to four and sixpence in the pound with an accompanying increase in surtax. He also suggests a future tax on land values – a proposal which sends shivers down our spines at Vine's Farm. How on earth can anyone defend further exaction upon an industry that has been in decline for a decade?

In May 1930 the Cabinet rejects Mosley's proposals and he resigns in protest. By July unemployment reaches two million. During the autumn Mosley appeals to the Labour Party Conference, but he is defeated again. Unemployment passes two and a half million by the year's end.

In February 1931 Mosley's patience snaps and he forms the New Party, which leads to his expulsion from the Labour movement. During the summer a committee on finance and industry, set up by the Treasury, issues a report. Its findings reveal a negative balance of payments with the rest of the world. Our country has relied on invisible earnings, such as banking, insurance and shipping, to put us in balance, and these fields of activity have been hit seriously by the Depression. The primary weapons identified to offset this problem are unsurprisingly increased taxation and reductions in public expenditure.

Having been recalled to London from his August vacation, the Prime Minister, Ramsay MacDonald, is informed by the Bank of England that there is now a run on the pound. This wave of selling sterling does not emanate from our budget deficit, negative balance of payments or unemployment. It has occurred through London bankers' generous long-term lending to Central Europe using French deposits. Following the war there has been no love lost between France and Germany – understandable perhaps since French military casualties were so high and much of the country's territory was obliterated into a moonscape. I can well see why France objects to lending money to the City for a return of two per cent when that same cash can be lent to the Germans at anything up to ten per cent. Consequently there have been many French withdrawals of currency from London and the pound is in danger of collapsing. To make matters worse, there is now a financial crisis in Central Europe. Germany has repudiated its international liabilities with a moratorium resulting in British money being frozen there. Put into perspective, all this financial woe renders our economic worries at Vine's Farm very small beer.

The Labour government looks as though it could be in its death throes because its ministers cannot agree on how to tackle this huge problem. There are, for example, internal objections to a ten-per-cent cut in unemployment benefit as a measure for balancing the budget.

On 24 August a national government is formed – a coalition of

Labour, Conservative and Liberal politicians. Ramsay MacDonald remains as Prime Minister, but he is accused of betrayal by many of his socialist colleagues. Philip Snowden, too, retains his position as Chancellor of the Exchequer. The new Cabinet comprises only ten members: four Labour, four Conservative and two Liberal.

A coalition administration served us well during the latter part of the war and it remains to be seen whether this initiative will save us in peacetime. Cuts in public expenditure are now having devastating effects upon the most vulnerable people in our society. On 15 September lower-deck personnel of the Atlantic Fleet mutiny at Invergordon. The pay of naval ratings has been cut in some cases by more than ten per cent. Although the men declare their loyalty to the Crown, they are refusing to put to sea until their grievances are addressed. The Admiralty promises a pay revision, and the government restricts all public expenditure cuts to ten per cent.

Nothing the government has done, however, arrests the run on our currency. On 19 September the Bank of England announces that foreign credits are exhausted. Two days later the coalition passes emergency legislation to abandon the gold standard, which had been restored in 1925 following an earlier suspension in 1919. The pound falls by over a quarter on international markets, but it seems that a wise decision has been made. We have been using paper £1 and ten-shilling notes since the outbreak of war in 1914 and they have always appeared to buy the same goods domestically as one could expect from gold sovereigns and half sovereigns. Now that our banknotes are unsupported by gold, their purchasing power remains undiminished at home. One benefit of the pound falling on international markets is that our exports become cheaper, and I do wonder whether we have hit upon an expedient which ultimately will bring us economic recovery.

So we are now in an age of a managed currency, where our government is not constricted by the international value of a precious metal. Of course there are dangers as a nation that prints too much money is likely to cause inflation. We saw this error committed in the aftermath of war, when some European countries did not balance their budgets and printed money to cover the shortfall. The resulting currency depreciation was felt particularly in Germany, where cash became almost worthless. There exists the anecdote of someone accidentally leaving a bag of Deutschmarks on a pavement only to discover later that the bag had gone while the money remained!

My husband, David, complains that I am becoming too wrapped up in matters political and suggests that my marrying him has compromised a latent ambition to pursue a career in Parliament. I tell him not to be so silly. My interest in politics stems merely from a protracted wait to gain the franchise and a desire for government to address the depressed condition of British agriculture. David does not look convinced. I explain further that, if my father is kind enough to pass his *Times* newspaper on to us, then I should very much like to understand the basics of what I read. When I become confused, Poppa is only too willing to elucidate for me. I consider this to be a valuable extension of my education.

I remind David of our most recent visit to the cinema some weeks earlier when we viewed Lilian's first talking picture, a jolly musical in which she sang, danced and acted. It provided just the sort of escapism which a downtrodden country needs. In marked contrast was the newsreel, in which Ramsay MacDonald appeared on screen to announce in his dour Scottish accent that "The nation is in trouble" but "It is only temporary, only temporary."

"You see, David, I believe it's important to know why the nation's in trouble and how we can get out of it."

"Well," my husband replies somewhat sardonically, "if you do know these things, then perhaps you ought to be in Parliament."

I retort that I am quite content to be an informed farmer's wife and a mother.

He smiles and puts his arm around my waist.

Lilian's second talkie is vastly different from her first. She has a straight acting role in a film simply called *Unwanted*. Although both the work and Lilian's performance are received with critical acclaim, there is little enthusiasm at the box office. It is easy to see why. At a time of national slump I cannot think of a more depressing film to be put before the public.

Lilian plays a working-class housewife whose domestic

circumstances take a turn for the worse when her husband loses his job. He cannot find employment anywhere and he gradually becomes a broken man whose only solace is alcohol paid for out of the small national assistance they receive. Lilian's character tries to supplement the dole by taking in washing – an occupation which makes it all the more difficult for her to look after her young family. Somehow she manages to cope in a life of drudgery until her husband, in a drunken stupor, kills their children and then himself while she is out of the house. This tragedy results in Lilian having a mental breakdown. No longer able to support herself, behind with the rent and facing eviction, she resorts to the oldest profession in the world only to discover that she is no longer attractive to men. Like her husband before her, she has become one of the 'unwanted'. The film ends with Lilian dying of hunger in the gutter as she vainly attempts to ply her trade. It is night-time and rain pours down relentlessly upon her as though to wash the problem into oblivion.

Along with everyone else, David and I are silent as we emerge from the picture house.

Once inside the milk van we have used for transport, I turn to my husband and whisper in his ear, "You do love me, don't you, darling?"

"More than ever," he answers softly. "Let's go home."

My daughter, Becky, is now seven and she has been attending the junior department at Endacott for two years. She is driven there and back by my father in his Morris Isis – a considerable improvement upon his previous motor car. The Morris is hard-topped and powerful, yet not quite as prestigious as Lilian's Lagonda or even Henry's Wolseley. It nevertheless provides a safe and comfortable ride.

Becky is happy at school – and so she should be with a doting grandfather who pays her educational fees and supplies transport over a distance which I consider to be beyond the call not only of duty, but also of generosity.

In October the national government goes to the country to seek a mandate. I vote for the second time in my life and stay loyal to our local MP. A turnout of sixty-seven per cent is the largest for a general election since the war. Those candidates standing on the national ticket take 554 of the 615 seats; 473 of these are won by the Conservatives while only fifty-two are won by Labour. It is somewhat ironic therefore that Ramsay MacDonald is to continue as Prime Minister.

This wretched year of 1931 – quite the worst of the Depression so far – is not yet done, but a piece of good news is forthcoming at Vine's Farm. Rosie, our milkmaid, is pregnant. She and her husband, Bill, who drives the better of our two milk vans, are thrilled. Rosie has developed in all respects from the rather simple fifteen-year-old I first encountered when she was Clara's housemaid. Now twenty-eight and married for seven years, she had begun to resign herself to childlessness. For my own part I am thirty-one and consider it unlikely I shall have another confinement, so I offer Rosie the pram and pushchair given to me by Lilian and Dotty respectively. Rosie is delighted.

Our milkmaid's pregnancy, however, provides us with a headache. We shall need a replacement in the dairy. There is no obvious candidate known to us in the community, but an unexpected letter, addressed to me, suggests a solution.

It is a sad correspondence which tells a tale so redolent of recent months. The author is Stella, that cheery Cockney land girl who taught me how to hand-milk a cow and so wonderfully smoothed my transition from ex-Endacott sixth-former to farmer's wife. We have exchanged Christmas cards each year since her departure, but this is the first missive which has passed between us.

Stella, like so many of our generation, has not found a husband, and now she has been unemployed for several weeks and is behind with the rent for her lodgings. Life has not been kind to her since returning to her native London, and the future looks bleaker than ever. She wonders whether there is any possibility of coming back to Vine's Farm. Well, of course there is! I run out to the yard, where David is helping our dairyman, George Akehurst, to clear slurry from the milking parlour.

"Our problem is solved!" I exclaim.

David reads Stella's letter.

"Sounds all right to me," he answers, "but where can she stay?"

"With us, of course. I'll clear it with Clara."

David nods his approval and his mother is also content. So I write to Stella an epistle of great joy and enclose a postal order to cover her train fare.

A week later I borrow the newer milk van and drive to our local station to await Stella's train. As I stand on the lonely platform I recall the occasion eleven years ago when she and I said goodbye at this very location. How sad we were then that we were parting, and how I missed her happy disposition which so assuaged the harshness of farming life!

I feel my heart racing a little as I discern a wisp of smoke in the distance. Soon the locomotive and carriages come into view and the train rumbles into the station. Only one passenger alights and slams the compartment door behind her. There stands Stella clutching a single suitcase. I assume it is Stella because steam from the engine has only just begun to clear.

I walk towards her as the guard's whistle blows and a green flag is waved to signal the driver to move off. The locomotive, now energised, puffs its way forward, and soon passenger and I are left alone in the peace of the Sussex countryside. The woman before me I do not recognise as the Stella of old. Her once rosy cheeks have given way to a grey pallor and her shoulders are slumped as though indicative of an undeserved hopelessness.

"Stella!" I cry, seemingly oblivious to her unprepossessing appearance.

"Hello, Vera," she responds in a quiet, defeated voice. "You haven't changed a bit."

"Oh, I don't know. I suppose I could find a grey hair or two if I looked closely enough."

Stella tries unsuccessfully to fashion a smile. I hold out my arms to embrace her and she bursts into tears. We hug each other for several seconds.

"The London I knew once", she begins, "is not the London I know now. It has become a very cruel place for some of us."

"You won't find any cruelty down here," I tell her. "I'm going to take you home, where we'll feed you up with healthy home-grown food. We'll put that colour back into those cheeks in no time."

I take her suitcase.

"I can carry that," she protests.

"You won't have to carry anything until you're fit and well."

Everything Stella owns, apart from the clothes on her back, is contained within the solitary item of luggage she has brought with her. Only a few shillings remain in her purse. Despite all our difficulties in running the farm and paying the mortgage, I feel like a millionaire.

Towards the end of the year another letter arrives at Vine's Farm –this time for David. It is typewritten, which always fills us with foreboding as it smacks of officialdom and financial worry.

The letter is from Henry and therefore is probably typed by Dotty. It is the shortest correspondence I have ever received, comprising just one sentence: 'Now is the time to strike.'

"What is he saying?" queries David. "Is he suggesting all British farmers should withdraw their labour in protest at the slump?"

I pause before answering: "Don't you remember, darling, two years ago when he and Dotty visited us? He said that we should consider buying Mill Farm when the price of land had bottomed out. He said that was the time to strike."

"Oh."

CHAPTER 19

THE TIME TO STRIKE

I feel so depressed by the economic events of 1931 that I write to both Lilian and Dotty inviting them and Henry to spend Christmas with us. I am not confident of receiving their acceptances to stay during winter in a house with no bathroom or electricity. They all enjoy lives with every modern convenience – something which can only remain an aspiration here until the national grid reaches us.

Notwithstanding the privations of Vine's Farm, they all agree to come. Lilian will arrive on Christmas Eve while Dotty and her husband will motor down a day earlier. Lilian has shut up Honeysuckle Cottage for the winter months and she is preparing for a new West End play scheduled to open in late February. She desires to free herself briefly from the bustle of London and sends forward apologies if she spends much of the holiday immersed in her script.

Stella is regaining strength and confidence. We treat her almost like one of the family, and my children have come to regard her as a newly found auntie. She will start working in the dairy once the New Year dawns. In the meantime she has sought to make herself useful by helping Clara and me in the house. Stella has volunteered to ensure that our seasonal guests are given every consideration, including the provision of log fires in their bedrooms.

So it is a very warm and welcoming farmhouse which greets Dotty and Henry on 23 December. I have been made aware of the fact that they like coming here despite the lack of amenities mainly because they love the home-grown food which adorns our dining table.

"Good, wholesome farmhouse cooking!" enthuses Henry. "You can't beat it."

Following lunch, he takes David and me aside.

"I got your letter of reply. Sorry mine was a bit terse, but I guessed you'd understand it. You say that you can't afford to buy Mill Farm, not even with a mortgage?"

"It's out of the question," sighs David. "Frankly, the place is something of a liability and nobody else wants to take it on."

Henry avers that economic depression, while a misery for many, is an opportunity for the few.

"Land's never been so cheap," he declares. "Why, in the main corn-growing areas some farms have actually been abandoned. If a man grows an acre of wheat, he loses £5. What's the point of that?"

"Precisely," answers David. "No point at all, so why buy more land?"

"Because some land can be bought for as little as £5 an acre."

"Well, that's as may be," I interject, "but what's the point of buying something which is useless?"

"Because it won't be useless for much longer."

"How do you know?"

Henry lights a cigar.

"Both of you, just think for a moment. In any industry things can go downhill for several years, but eventually there comes a time when entry into that industry is so cheap that it becomes an opportunity for investment. I don't want to be impertinent, and you can tell me to mind my own business if you wish, but how much per acre did you pay for Vine's Farm and when did you buy it?"

David and I look nervously at each other.

"Er, £30 an acre in 1919," returns my husband, "which was cheap. Lord Cloudsley originally wanted £40."

Henry blows smoke from his cigar.

"Doesn't look that cheap now, does it?"

"Well, there's no need to rub it in," groans David guiltily.

"Look – I'm not trying to rub anything in. Consider it this way: Vine's Farm and Mill Farm are roughly the same size and have the same kind of soil. If you bought Mill Farm at £5 an acre, all told you would have purchased 300 acres at an average price of, what, £17 ten shillings per acre. Doesn't sound so bad now, does it?"

I re-enter the conversation: "This sounds all very well, Henry, but we occupy Mill Farm already and we can't do much with it unless we lose money."

"Which, my dear, is why you could purchase it so cheaply."

"But that would cost us money we don't have, and all we'd acquire is a white elephant."

"Not for long."

David rejoins the discussion: "Henry, Vera has already asked you how you know this, but you've ducked the question."

"All right, I'll duck it no more. Farming has been in depression for over a decade. The rest of British industry has only been in the doldrums for a couple of years. The Labour government hadn't a clue how to sort out the mess, so it went into coalition with the Tories and Liberals. We now have a national government dedicated to getting the economy back on track. Do you suppose they will try to save every industry except agriculture?"

"Well, frankly, yes," responds David pessimistically.

"I can understand your cynicism," Henry continues, "but I think you're wrong. The government will be at pains to address the woes of all parts of the nation, and not just bits of it; otherwise current discontent will escalate. It's a national government which depends for its credibility on saving the countryside as well as the towns and cities. You must have noticed how corn prices have slumped drastically in the last twelve months alone. There'll be something in it for the farmers, you mark my words."

David and I believe it is easy for someone outside our industry to be sanguine about its prospects, but we congratulate Henry for putting his argument well. The matter is, however, academic since we do not have the financial means necessary to contemplate purchase of Mill Farm. In any event, we doubt whether the bank would sell the property for such a ridiculously low figure as £5 an acre.

"Has anyone offered anything for it?" retorts Henry.

"Not as far as we know," David advises.

"Indeed, the fact is they can't sell, yet they're desperate to raise capital on the asset. How long has it been on the market?"

"Over three years," I confess.

"I guessed as much. Dotty and I noticed paint peeling on the 'For Sale' sign as we drove by. Incidentally, it's partly fallen down, hanging at twenty degrees, I'd say."

"I'll tell the agents."

"Better to make them an offer, Vera."

"We've nothing to offer them!" I exclaim.

"I have," declares Henry.

"I didn't think you wanted to buy a farm," David remarks.

"I don't, but I'll finance you."

"Henry," I protest, "we can't possibly accept charity."

"I'm not offering it," he states bluntly. "I'm a businessman and I'm suggesting a business proposition."

"How do you mean?" enquires David.

"Let me be your mortgagee at a rate of interest more favourable to you than any bank would countenance. You don't need the farmhouse at Mill Farm, so tempt the bank by saying they can sell it separately. It should find a buyer more easily then. Offer £5 an acre for the remainder, take it or leave it, and say your offer remains open for no more than a month."

David and I look at each other askance.

"I don't get it," my husband queries at length. "What's in it for you, Henry?"

"Although it'd be a cheap loan, you'd be paying me more than a bank would on deposit."

"Suppose we defaulted on the mortgage?" I enquire. "You'd be saddled with a farm you don't want and couldn't sell."

Henry fixes his eyes upon me.

"I certainly wouldn't want it, but I'd be well placed to sell it at a profit."

"You seem very sure farming's going to have an upturn," remarks David.

"I think it's bottomed out," Henry asserts, "along with everything else. The only way is up, even if the climb is slow."

David remains to be convinced.

"Even if you're right, Henry, why should you wish to back Vera and me?"

Our guest expels more cigar smoke into the room.

"Well, apart from the fact that you're friends and I trust you, I see a lot of ex-soldiers who volunteered in our country's time of need. Many of them are now unemployed or doing jobs below their station to make ends meet. I'll give you an example. Despite the Depression, my firm had a vacancy for a junior clerk. I made the mistake of advertising the post in one of the London evening papers. The next morning a queue formed outside our offices, down two flights of stairs and into the street for several blocks. The police had to be called in case of trouble. I needn't have worried. When word passed back along the line that we were only going to interview the first half-dozen, the rest just turned and moved silently away. They were beaten men, you see. They had no fight left in them – it had all been sucked away by months of hopelessness – yet they turned up just in case, and one fellow was lucky. I filled this rather menial position with a man who'd commanded an infantry company during the war. He reached the rank of major and even won a Military Cross, but he was now content to take a job one would normally give to a youngster. You're an ex-soldier, David. You fought in the trenches and contracted a shrapnel wound from which you still suffer today. Like so many fellows, yours was not a good war. I did have a good war. I was involved in army procurement. I never left these shores and I swanned about in uniform, finishing up as a lieutenant colonel. Thus I was protected not only from the Boche, but also from those damn silly women who went about handing out white feathers to people. Now I have an opportunity to help someone who got the dirty end of army life and doesn't spend the rest of his time moaning about it. The offer's on the table, and it's up to you and Vera whether you wish to take advantage of it. One word of advice: don't take too long to make up your minds. Things might start to move quickly in the weeks ahead."

I leave David and Henry to continue their conversation and repair to the dining room, where Dotty is putting away cutlery having assisted Clara and Stella with the washing-up.

159

"I don't expect a guest to do that," I tell her.

"I know," she grins. "That's why I'm doing it!"

Shutting a drawer of the sideboard, Dotty adopts a more thoughtful expression.

"Has Henry been talking about Mill Farm?"

"He's mentioned the proposition to you, then?"

"Yes, and, though I shouldn't say so, it is a fact that my husband has the ear of a few people in high places. I'm not trying to boast, but he's a member of quite an exclusive club where the odd tongue loosens after a drink or two. Take it from me, it looks as if the government might be giving a boost to agriculture in the very near future. Whatever you do, don't tell anyone except David that I've said anything to you about this."

Well, I like to think that I am not one to gossip, so I do not broach the subject of Mill Farm again that day. Rather I am looking forward to seeing Lilian once more.

She arrives in her Lagonda on the morrow, and I am both surprised and disappointed that she does not seem to be her usual ebullient self. I learn that she is suffering from the disappointing response to her film *Unwanted*.

"I had such high hopes for it," she laments.

I reveal that David and I saw the picture.

"It was a superb piece of work," I tell her, "and you were brilliant in it. I needed my handkerchief throughout. I just think the film was released at the wrong time. The whole country's so depressed, it doesn't want to be depressed further. Once everyone's on their feet again, they'll look upon this picture as a classic – one that teaches—"

"The posh word is *didactic*," Lilian interjects. "I agree; but if one puts it back in the can for five years and then re-releases it, there will only be a small audience of connoisseurs. The fact is we put a lot of effort into *Unwanted* and it has turned out to be the most aptly named thing I've ever done."

Oh dear – poor Lilian! I do hope that we can cheer her up this Christmas.

It comes to pass that the two people who do more than anyone to rejuvenate her spirits are my children, James and Becky. What is even more remarkable is the fact that, rather than distracting Lilian from learning her thespian lines, they are both instrumental in helping her to achieve her objective. A ten-year-old boy and seven-year-old girl sit on our sofa with a script held between them. James is reading a male part while Becky is assigned a female role. Lilian stands in the middle of the room delivering her lines from memory and hamming it up for all she is worth. The play is a comedy and thus an aid to the jollity which emanates whenever Lilian's memory fails her. Becky, in particular, shrieks with laughter every time the professional actress stumbles.

"You little monkey!" Lilian declares. "You're trying to put me off!"

In truth Becky is besotted by her 'Aunt Lilian' and wishes to emulate her. She has stars in her eyes and tells everyone at school that she knows a famous person of stage and screen. When she informs Lilian that her friends do not believe her, the subject of her hero worship reveals a surprise.

"Don't say anything about this to anyone at Endacott yet, but I've been asked to be the guest of honour at next year's prize-giving."

Becky looks as though she has just received her best Christmas present.

"Now," continues Lilian, "I shall make a point of telling all your friends that I know you very well and sometimes you help me to learn my lines."

Seeing Lilian with James and Becky, I am saddened that she has not married and started a family. I suppose it must be almost impossible to have a career like hers and combine it with domestic bliss. It is a dilemma which so afflicts the female of the species. Despite the dearth of available men in our generation, I doubt that a woman so attractive as Lilian, both in looks and talent, would have any difficulty in securing a mate. For the moment, however, she ploughs a lone furrow in life.

Our festive evenings under oil lamps would be incomplete without music, so I am recruited yet again to play the piano as accompaniment to Lilian's singing. Amongst other numbers, she chooses 'Tea for Two' and sings it to young James, who appears suitably embarrassed but takes it in good part.

My brother Edwin, who will be twenty-six in February, has been articled to a firm of solicitors for some years and he has now qualified. He is to enter my father's own practice in the new year. Edwin is living with my parents for the time being, and the three of them join us for Christmas Day and Boxing Day. Truly, during this Yuletide Vine's Farm is a bustling and jolly place. I just hope 1932 gives us all cause to remain sanguine.

CHAPTER 20

WE STRIKE

As we move into that deflated mood often associated with the aftermath of festive celebration, there is one matter which dominates our thoughts. It dominates because Henry has emphasised urgency and we are denied that temporal comfort of being able to act at our convenience.

Levied against this desire for extended contemplation is the fear that we may rush into something foolish or become complacent and miss the opportunity of a lifetime. Clara, however, remains rooted in the notion that we should have no ambitions for the future of Mill Farm.

"Leave well alone" is the oft-repeated mantra from my mother-in-law.

The question arises as to what we should do with this additional acreage were we to buy it. We cover the same old ground we tilled when deliberating whether to occupy Mill Farm while the bank sought a purchaser. The blunt truth remains: we lack the capital to expand our current farming policy to an area twice the size of our existing holding. Even if we were able to double the dairy herd, there seems little scope to enlarge our retailing activity. We operate in a rural area with only one small market town within daily deliverable reach.

David put this argument to Henry during Christmas, but Dotty's husband remained adamant that we should make a low offer to purchase the neighbouring property. We consider it highly unlikely that a successful businessman and friend like Henry would act as mortgagee in a venture which was anything other than an attractive proposition.

So what is it he knows, or thinks he knows? Clearly he has intimated something to Dotty which encourages her to believe that there is an advantage to be had. I have valued Dotty's friendship over many years now and I am confident she would never dream of supporting any action which might operate to my detriment.

David and I wrestle with this problem during almost every waking hour, including when lying in bed before attempting to fall asleep. There comes a point when we both realise that we are just repeating ourselves and there seems little profit in discussing the pros and cons any further. The time has come when we must 'strike', to use Henry's expression, or just abandon the whole issue. Having taken note of Henry's suggestion that we should put in what might seem an insultingly low offer, we resolve to strike.

Our tender is submitted in writing and there is no expectation that the matter will be taken further by the bank. Within a week, however, my husband and I are sitting in Mr Lamacraft's office and observing his reaction to our proposal.

"Forgive me, Mr Coulthurst, but you can hardly expect the bank to countenance such an offer. I think it eminently sensible that having farmed the land for, what, three and a half years now, you see the benefits of combining the two farms into one holding. Any offer you make, however, must be realistic. I mean, £5 per acre, to include all the buildings, excepting the house, is, if you pardon me, ridiculous."

"Have you had any better offers, Mr Lamacraft?"

David retains an expression as stony as that of his addressee.

"Er, I'm not of course at liberty to divulge any proposals put forward by a third party. Suffice it to say that we have not received an offer to date which the bank considers is a basis for negotiation."

"Which is just as well," retorts David, "because my wife and I are not going to negotiate anything ourselves. Our offer, subject to contract, is on the table and we can only leave it there for one month. Remember, we're not requiring the house. We already have a place to live. That house at Mill Farm would fetch a good price without the burden of 150 acres around it which nobody else seems to want."

The bank manager looks perplexed. It is that same expression he displayed when we enunciated the terms under which we agreed to rent the property in 1928. His verbal response follows the same pattern as it did then.

"You understand, of course, that I am not authorised to accept or refuse your offer. All I can do is refer it up the line, so to speak. Frankly, though, I doubt whether my superiors will give you a favourable answer."

So we leave it there. I write to Dotty and ask her to tell Henry what we have done. She writes back to say that her husband believes we have acted wisely. All we can do now is wait.

We expect a protracted delay not dissimilar to that encountered prior to our tenancy. Our expectations, however, prove to be unfounded. With almost alarming haste the bank accepts our offer. Fear and doubt now overtake us as David and I try to come to terms with events.

"It is often said in farming", my husband remarks in an attempt to be positive, "that first loss is best loss."

I ask whether the bank knows something we do not. According to Henry we are supposed to know something of which the bank is ignorant – an unlikely scenario. We then discuss whether the bank will actually lose anything. There will have been mortgage repayments made by the Patemans over several years, of course. Undoubtedly the most valuable asset at Mill Farm is the house, which can be sold for whatever the market will stand. There exists a demand for fairly substantial dwellings in the countryside within a short distance of the railway, particularly if they are accompanied by ample gardens. Maybe this is the key to an early decision. Five pounds an acre nevertheless seems inordinately cheap as it includes the farm buildings and two admittedly rather squalid workers' cottages. It does not help, however, that Clara remains unmoved in her opposition to our strategy.

David writes to Henry, who confirms that he will make £750 available to us at an annual interest rate of three and a half per cent over thirty years with an option to redeem the loan earlier if we so desire. He instructs his solicitors to draw up a mortgage contract which will be sent to my father, who will act for us.

Dearest Poppa will not hear of charging us a fee, yet we owe him so much already. I have sought his opinion on our new venture on several occasions. He gives me comfort by saying that it can rarely be wrong to buy at the bottom of a market and that, even by today's standards, Mill Farm is ridiculously cheap.

"Fortunately, my dear," he explains, "you are buying from an institution which has been trying to get rid of the property for far too long. You're in the right place at the right time. Henry is correct in saying that you'll scarcely have another opportunity like this in your own lifetime. If the fortunes of agriculture turn about, you'll be in a very strong position."

So my father, whose views I always value, is supportive. I do not think that I could go through with this business without his favourable analysis.

Dotty reinforces Poppa's positive stance by writing me a letter in which she reveals that we are doubling the size of our farm for the price of a modern pebble-dashed three-bedroom semi-detached house in the London suburbs.

I relate all this to Clara, whose lugubrious attitude to our purchase shows no sign of changing. I suppose one's view is predicated on whether one is on the outside looking in or on the inside looking out. Like my mother-in-law, I am looking out and wondering why the bank threw in the towel so readily. David tries to reassure me by suggesting that the vendors wanted to free up capital to do what banks do best.

"I'll warrant they've had no better offers for at least two years," he says, "so what's the point of hanging on any longer?"

Stella has been reunited with George Akehurst, our dairyman, and she is impressed by how Rosie has transformed herself from the gauche adolescent she knew during and just after the war. Stella's biggest surprise, however, is the milking machine. Now it is Rosie who must instruct her elder in its operation. Stella will also have to be familiarised with the bottling machinery. Farming, even in our relatively small enterprise, does not stand still.

The sale of Mill Farm goes through to completion and we are now the proud owners of a combined holding totalling 300 acres. Chins wag and ears twitch in the local community. Rumour has it that the Coulthursts have come into money or have become so carried away with some minor success in their unorthodox farming policy that they have acquired ideas beyond their station.

No matter – we have to decide what to do with our additional acres now we hold title to them. This is no easy decision as we have precious little working capital and the depressed condition of our calling has shown no sign of improving.

Then it happens. The national government announces that something must be done to address the abysmal returns for wheat growing. The politicians resolve to provide relief for near-bankrupt wheat farmers, predominantly in the English eastern counties, where the better soils lend themselves well to growing the crop. Certainly the problem needs addressing because the wheat price has fallen to five shillings and eight pence per hundredweight when it had not been below nine shillings between 1922 and 1930.

So we are to have the Wheat Act. It is a piece of legislation which emanates from the government's recent renunciation of free trade. While protectionism is not generally a popular policy, our country is in such a parlous position economically that drastic measures are considered necessary.

The aim of the bill going through Parliament is to provide British farmers with a secure market and enhanced price for millable wheat without government subsidy, and to do so without encouraging farmers to grow the crop on unsuitable land. David and I are concerned that our Weald clay may be deemed unsuitable by the powers that be, particularly as we cannot hope to compete with growers on the silts and loams, which can only be looked upon with envy. It is on such soils that yields of up to one and a half tons per acre can be achieved. We are lucky to get half that amount in a good year.

The national government intends to finance this interventionist initiative through imposing duties on wheat imports and levies on all sales of flour. Money raised in this way is to be distributed to wheat growers in the form of 'deficiency payments'. There is to be one of these payments each year. It is to be determined by calculating the difference between the average market price at the end of each cereal year on 31 July and a 'standard price' to

167

be set at ten shillings per hundredweight, equating to forty-five shillings per quarter.

In the Commons debate on the Wheat Bill, one of my political heroines, Nancy Astor, disappoints me by asking whether setting the standard price so high is likely to encourage farmers to grow wheat when they have never grown it previously and in so doing will never grow it economically. No doubt she is thinking of more marginal land, like our own. For the first time in my life I wish she would shut up.

The Minister of Agriculture responds with a supercilious air, saying, "The noble lady must not assume anything of the kind."

I could not have put it better myself!

The Act receives its royal ascent on 12 May. Notwithstanding our inferior heavy ground, David and I have glints in our eyes.

"So Henry came home for us," my husband enthuses.

"I wonder how he knew," I reply.

"Who cares, Vera? This could be the turnaround British farming needs. It tells us what to do with at least some of the Mill Farm land, whether Lady Astor likes it or not!"

The fact is that we should have had to sow a little wheat this coming autumn even if the new Act had not been passed. We last grew the crop in 1928, and we retained enough wheat to feed our chickens for a few years thence. This supply will only last another twelve months. We have been storing it in several galvanised steel bins, which keep the grain in good condition provided its moisture is low.

Now wheat has become a marginally economic proposition on land which our national legislators might deem unsuitable. We therefore resolve to sow winter wheat initially on most of the Mill Farm fields, leaving in grass a few which had provided good-quality swards when we took over from the Patemans – fields which are both stock-proof and possessed of a water supply through pond or well.

One cannot, however, grow white straw crops year after year on the same ground without exhausting the soil and suffering poor yields. There remains therefore the issue of rotation and maintaining fertility. We cannot afford artificial manures, and, in any event, they are not as effective as livestock dung. David quips that one has to have a sense of humus in farming – a remark for which I feel obliged to offer him a sympathetic smile.

We decide to move our beef cattle and folded poultry on to Mill Farm pastures. All dung from the winter quarters of our dairy and beef cattle, together with slurry from the milking parlour, is to be applied as far as it will go to fields destined for wheat just prior to ploughing. We take a hay crop from all non-grazed grassland during this first year. Manuring of Vine's Farm is restricted to the grazing of our dairy cows.

Looking to the future, we settle on a rotation of two years' wheat, two years' grass. This will necessitate some adjustment after the farming year 1932–33. We shall be growing more wheat during this first year than subsequently. The purpose is to take advantage of the fact that Mill Farm has had a rest from arable cropping since 1928 and thereby we will be able to generate more cash from the enhanced price of wheat.

When the initial harvest is completed we shall have to divide the Mill Farm land into four quarters, ensuring there are enough stock-proof fields supplied with water and left in grass to accommodate our poultry and beef cattle. This requirement must be satisfied year on year. The rotational plan is first wheat, second wheat, grass for hay, pasture. In this way the grazed land, made fertile through the droppings of cattle or chickens, will come under the plough in readiness for the first wheat. The fields destined for the second wheat will, as far as possible, receive dung and slurry from the buildings of both farms. The grass for hay will be sown after harvesting the second wheat. We shall include clover in the seed mix because, being a legume, it will fix nitrogen from the air and be an aid to fertility. Removing hay from a field, as with straw from cereal crops, depletes phosphorus and potash so the grass is only grazed in its second year to enable the soil to recover.

So we have a four-course rotation of sorts – not the traditional four-course rotation of wheat, oats or barley, clover and roots, but what can only be called a Coulthurst rotation, which David and I both suspect will earn rustic opprobrium for miles around!

169

We toyed with the notion of saving money by letting second wheat stubbles tumble down to grass, but we have abandoned this thought on the grounds that we need clover to help maintain soil fertility and thereby provide better crops and grazing.

It is a great relief to be able to grow wheat at even a small profit, not least because we have spent four years producing excessive amounts of indifferent-quality hay from Mill Farm. Much of this crop has proved difficult to shift. We have sold what we could, often at prices below the cost of production. Any surplus which we were unable to utilise as feed has been used as litter when running short of straw from our small barley crop at Vine's Farm. Moving straw-based dung by hand is hard enough, but forking out manure made with hay is beyond a joke. It is much heavier and more difficult for the fork to penetrate. We can thankfully now say goodbye to all that.

During early August Rosie gives birth to a healthy son weighing over eight pounds. She and Bill are thrilled, and we all get to see the new arrival, who, in view of his size, is already being assessed as a potential candidate for farmwork!

On the subject of labour, our dear tractor, Beatrice, which David tends with almost as much loving care as Rosie affords baby Keith, will be busier than ever this autumn. She is our sole power source on the land and we dread anything going wrong with her at cultivating and sowing time. Of course we should like a second tractor to speed the work before the rains come, and to enable us to keep going in the event of mechanical failure, but this can only be a pipe dream at present.

Autumn therefore heralds an almost frenetic period as we set about drilling some 120 acres of winter wheat. It is during this effort that Lilian is due to present the Speech Day prizes at Endacott College. She will address the whole school, and Becky is excited at the prospect of proving to her classmates that the great Lilian Cairns is her pretend auntie.

Parents are invited to attend, and it is in this capacity that I accompany Lilian to our alma mater. David is far too busy with arable work and tenders his apologies. Lilian collects me after lunch from Vine's Farm in her powerful Lagonda, and we roar along country lanes to cover the twenty-mile journey. We are to bring Becky back with us, thereby saving my father the trouble.

Speech Day is an important event in the Endacott calendar. Pupils are expected to be on their best behaviour, and each girl is inspected for tidiness by Miss Buckmaster, the headmistress, as they file into the school hall. I recall unforgivably having had a button undone many years ago. The reprimand I received is indelibly imprinted on my mind, to the extent that I regularly check my buttons whenever I am going out. I check them this morning and mention the fact to Lilian, who almost loses control of the car as we speed to our destination.

My memories of Speech Day are of sitting, without fidgeting, while some notable worthy expounded interminable platitudes from the stage. Miss Buckmaster, seated nearby, gave us all the impression that nothing but pearls of wisdom were emanating from the lips of our distinguished guest.

I suspect, however, that we may be about to experience a rare departure from this onerous tradition. Lilian could not be described as boring, unless tedium were required in playing a dramatic role. So it is proved. After rising to speak and waiting for the polite introductory applause to fade away, within seconds she has her largely juvenile audience in fits of laughter as she relates anecdotes from her acting and singing career. The stage is her world and the world is her stage. I observe from my vantage point that Miss Buckmaster has fixed a synthetic smile upon her countenance as though to approve of everything Lilian is saying, but in reality I suspect she does not.

Lilian concludes by advising the girls to keep their hockey sticks low and their aspirations high before returning to her chair amid rapturous applause, which continues far longer than our esteemed headmistress would like. Miss Buckmaster stands by the lectern nervously waiting for the cheering, shouting, laughing and clapping to abate. Eventually she has everyone's attention.

"Well, girls," she begins, "Miss Cairns has certainly regaled us with a robust, if unconventional, call to arms. She was the lifeblood of our drama and choir throughout her schooling with us, and I note the passage of time has not dampened any of her remarkable vigour."

In the wake of formalities, a light tea, prepared by domestic-science sixth-formers, is served to parents and staff by girls of divers ages. Despite her dearth of years, Becky has either volunteered or been coerced into being a waitress, and she, with a few of her friends, makes a beeline for Lilian and me. It is obvious that her main motivation is to show her companions that the guest of honour is well acquainted with Miss Rebecca Coulthurst.

Her mission accomplished, evidenced by the amazed expressions of the other girls, Becky invites us to sample the cucumber sandwiches. Another tray containing fancy cakes is soon thrust in our direction, and we are further encouraged to wash down this repast with a cup of tea.

Becky's euphoria is quickly dissipated, however, when Millicent Harper, our contemporary at school and now the classics mistress, approaches. Indeed, all juvenile countenances appear frozen with foreboding in the presence of the one-time Endacott swot.

"Lilian, Vera," greets the newcomer. "The three little maids seem to be one short."

This is a reference to the fact that Dotty and the two of us once played these roles in a school production of *The Mikado*.

"Dotty's not a parent or the guest speaker," I advise.

Millicent fashions a smile which I surmise must have taken no mean effort. She goes on to explain to my daughter and her friends that we three adults present were at Endacott together. I could almost burst out laughing at the shocked expressions displayed on these young faces as they digest this revelation.

Lilian and I are treated to a more verbal reaction from Becky as we drive home.

"Mummy, how can you and Auntie Lilian have been at school with Miss Harper? I mean, she must be at least 100!"

The autumn sowing at Mill Farm is completed before the expected rains saturate our clay soil into a condition whereby it cannot be traversed again until next spring. The remainder of the year settles back into a familiar routine of tending livestock and continuing with our retail deliveries.

The New Year dawns with our nation still in the grip of economic depression. This decade is already being dubbed 'the dirty thirties'. Conditions are bad here, and they are even worse in some other countries. Germany in particular has barely recovered from military defeat in 1918 notwithstanding a fleeting boom during the twenties. Now there is political turmoil in that troubled land. Pursuant to an election, a new Chancellor is appointed in late January. His name is Adolf Hitler.

CHAPTER 21

LIGHT AT THE END OF A DARK TUNNEL

Our purchase of Mill Farm has created a problem for Mr and Mrs Claxton, living in the farmhouse there. Understandably the bank wishes to sell the property as quickly as possible, particularly in the light of its disposing of the farm so cheaply.

I feel sorry for the Claxtons, who are such a delightful couple. We could not be provided with better neighbours. Their tenancy is about to expire, and they will have to vacate the property unless they can buy the dwelling, which sadly seems to be beyond their means.

At the eleventh hour, however, divine intervention rides to the rescue. As the tenancy expires, so comes word that Mrs Claxton's mother has done likewise, leaving her daughter the bungalow in Kent. While this single-storey residence alone cannot begin to defray the full cost of Mill House, an accompanying liquid legacy and the Claxtons' delving into their own savings all combine to realise a sum which is satisfactory to the vendor.

Mill House sells for £1,500, meaning the whole of Mill Farm has netted the bank £2,250. This seems a considerable loss when set against the sum which must have been advanced to the Patemans when they purchased the holding shortly after the war. This deficit can only have been reduced through mortgage repayments remitted by the borrowers. If the mortgagees had foreseen the 1932 Wheat Act, then I doubt we should be farming these acres as owner-occupiers with the Claxtons having a substantial home in the Sussex countryside.

There is more good news on the horizon. The national grid is coming to our area at last. We are to have a pylon in one of the

Mill Farm fields. Erection of this galvanised-steel structure has begun. The local consensus of opinion is that it is something of an eyesore, made worse by the line of pylons on either side of it, extending seemingly forever into the distance. I should imagine that arrival of the railway nearly ninety years ago must have sparked similar disgruntlement – an unwarranted intrusion into the pastoral scene of England. In truth, however, neither of these intrusions can be satisfactorily described as unwarranted. We need railways in a modern society to transport people and goods efficiently, and we need electric power if we are not to be condemned to living in a more primitive age with all its discomforts. I want to be done with oil lamps, cooking on a wood-fuelled range and having no room dedicated to one's ablutions with hot water immediately available. Bring me fully into the twentieth century, please!

My daughter, Becky, has let it be known that she is so happy at school that she wishes to board there from September. It was always my father's intention to facilitate this change financially when Becky was old enough – not least because it would save him the onerous daily task of transporting her. My daughter will be nine years old on 19 September, and I suppose this will not be too young given that she adores Endacott. I boarded there quite happily for five years, and now there is a junior department I see no reason why Becky should not do likewise for even longer, until she is eighteen.

Despite our relatively poor soil, it is good to observe wheat growing here again after an absence of several years. Poppies have emerged amongst our corn, studding the crop with crimson blobs. As harvest approaches, red and gold wave in unison with a gentle wind. Thirty years ago, in the main wheat-growing area of East Anglia, the local railway company advertised similar scenes as a tourist attraction, dubbing the countryside 'Poppyland'.

We cannot, of course, rival the yields in that part of the country, yet David estimates that we might achieve ten hundredweight or so per acre when our wheat is threshed out during late autumn or early winter.

Once the stubbles are cleared of stooks, and the latter are

safely ricked, we set about sowing some of these fields with a mixture of clover, ryegrass and timothy. The remaining stubbles, amounting to about one-quarter of the Mill Farm acreage, we prepare for a second wheat. A similar area of old grassland is ploughed for a first corn crop. Thereby we embark upon our rotation of two years' wheat followed by an identical period of grass. Local farming sages are saying that growing a second wheat will exhaust the soil, but, with organic matter being applied, we hope to prove them wrong.

The national government seems to have undergone a rural renaissance for, having given us the Wheat Act, it has now established the Milk Marketing Board. The purpose of this agency is to control national milk production and distribution. It is to function as a buyer of last resort, thereby guaranteeing a minimum price for milk producers such as ourselves. Things are looking up almost beyond our wildest dreams.

In the wake of this welcome initiative comes an unexpected opportunity. On the other side of our village there lives a man by the name of Bingo Crouch. For many years he and his long-suffering wife have eked out a living through hand-milking ten cows and selling their bounty to local inhabitants scattered over a fairly wide area connected by narrow winding lanes. It is a primitive enterprise, although Bingo has upgraded it to the extent that he bottles by hand and distributes his milk in much the same way as we do.

Late one afternoon he arrives at Vine's Farm in his battered Model T van – a vehicle of similar vintage to our Lizzy, yet indicative of having received much less in the way of care and attention.

"Af'noon, missus. Be the guvnor around?"

I inform him that anything he wishes to say to David he may tell me. No matter how many times I remind him of this truth, he insists on speaking to my husband. I really do find this habit of some men, wishing to exclude women from business conversations, a most irritating experience.

Reluctantly I repair to the implement shed, where David is fitting new shares to our plough.

"Bingo Crouch wants to speak with you."

David sighs in frustration.

"Doesn't the old goat know we're busy? Can't you deal with him?"

I advise David of my predicament. He drops his spanner in a manner suggestive of annoyance and, aided by his stick, hobbles behind me. It does not surprise me that he is in some discomfort from his war wound. This usually occurs when he has been crouching to perform some mechanical task or other. The problem also appears to manifest itself when he is inconvenienced.

"Well, what is it, Bingo? We've got a lot on at the moment."

As if oblivious to this fact, Mr Crouch launches into a lugubrious narrative about advancing years with associated bodily pains and fatigue as though my husband is innocent of such ailments.

"I don't wanna retire, but me old bones can't take much more."

"I'm sorry to hear it," David sympathises.

"Mebbe you won't be so sorry when you hears what I've got to propose."

"And what do you propose?"

"That you buys me out."

My husband and I try to absorb the full import of this statement.

"Buy you out?" queries David. "What do you mean exactly?"

"You buys me milk round. It's a good little business – it's kept me and the missus going for several year."

What is running through my mind at this juncture is the probability that the dairy in our market town would not wish to purchase Mr Crouch's round unless it first got its hands on ours. We control deliveries between village and town and within parts of the town itself. Mr Crouch operates on the wrong side of the village.

"So what are you offering precisely?" asks David.

"Me customer list and all the goodwill that goes with it."

"And how much are you asking?"

"Hundred and fifty pound."

"It isn't worth it."

"All right, 130 and I'll throw in all the crates and bottles."

"What about your van?"

"I was going to keep it for transport: £20!"

"It isn't worth ten. Look at it."

"It's never let me down."

David changes the subject: "So what about your farm? What is it – fifty acres?"

"Forty-five. I'm going to rent it out to the bloke next door."

"What about your cows?"

"People'll have to bid for 'em in the market."

I do not doubt that while this discourse is progressing David is weighing up the true value of Bingo's milk round. Out of respect for me and probably to irk the would-be vendor, my husband breaks off the conversation so that he and I may discuss matters privately.

"Now listen, Bingo," says David at length, "here's the deal. Your round with crates and bottles is worth no more than £100 to us and far less to anyone else. As an act of charity we'll give you £10 for the van. We want a detailed list of all your customers with an up-to-date account of who owes what. I suggest you get everyone to pay in full on your last day. Anything outstanding will come to us."

Mr Crouch does not look happy, but I think we have been fair with him. As it is we shall have much difficulty in raising the £110 offered.

"I'll have to talk it over with the missus," Bingo declares.

This is progress indeed, for I should imagine Mrs Crouch is not a woman regularly consulted by her husband. In any event, I suspect this delay is merely a ruse to give Bingo time to mull things over in his own mind.

We leave matters there; but within forty-eight hours Mr Crouch returns to accept our offer, albeit with an air of disgruntlement.

The van we have bought from him is an absolute heap. I take it for a test drive and return to the farm in a state of some anxiety.

"David, it's positively dangerous. I was all over the road. Fortunately I didn't meet anything else; otherwise I'm sure I would have had an accident!"

Wearily my husband clambers underneath and emerges with his diagnosis: "The track rod ends are worn out – both of them. We'll get some new ones and I'll fit them. I'll need to give this jalopy a good service."

I can only conclude that Bingo Crouch did not come to grief in this death trap because he drove slowly between deliveries and was used to the idiosyncrasies of his vehicle.

When David comes to fit the replacement track rod ends, he sends me on a mission to borrow a tape measure from Clara's needlework basket. Upon my return I learn the reason for this unusual errand.

"The front wheels have to toe in," David explains, "Otherwise the tyres will wear out unevenly."

"They look pretty worn out already, darling."

"Bingo's idea of a worn tyre is one with the cord showing. It's not worth spending too much money on this wreck. We'll make it safe for the time being. No doubt we'll have to replace it sooner rather than later."

David goes on to explain that using a tape measure is a very crude method of adjusting the front-wheel alignment. I feel much blessed, however, that he is able to undertake this task with the means at his disposal. I am required to assist him by holding one end of the tape at regular intervals while he holds the other before disappearing under the vehicle with a spanner.

We need Bingo's old van to cover his former milk round. Our other two Fords are fully occupied with their own duties. It has fallen to me to become Bingo's replacement, and I make myself known to his customers and apprise them of our additional services to supply eggs and potatoes. Our business has expanded again and we seem to have made a good bargain.

When events are going well there often emerges something unpleasant to remind us that our passage through life is not a journey which breeds eternal optimism. In the autumn of 1933 we suffer a tragedy at Vine's Farm. Rufus, our golden cocker spaniel, has died. In coming to terms with this loss we have to be pragmatic, for he had reached the amazing age of sixteen. Over so many years we never contemplated he would leave us, and we took his constant companionship for granted.

Born in 1917, Rufus arrived at Vine's Farm even before I

did. He was ostensibly a gun dog, but David's inability to walk very far without resting rendered Rufus largely a pet and he was loved by all. He was allowed to roam free around the farmyard and was therefore not short of exercise, and I remember when he accompanied me as I pushed my babies in their pram all those years ago. I weep for him.

I have to break the news of Rufus's demise to James and Becky, now both at boarding school. Becky, I know, will be distraught. The death of any animal on the farm brings her distress, and, of all the creatures here, Rufus was her favourite.

David has buried our best friend in one corner of the garden, and, with Becky in mind, has marked the spot with a wooden cross.

We resolve to find a replacement for Rufus and make enquiries both at the local market and with our milk-round customers. This strategy bears fruit when we learn that a golden cocker bitch has given birth to a litter of puppies all of whom resemble Rufus. When they are ready for sale we bring home a mischievous male, whose naming we leave to Becky. By letter she informs us that she has chosen 'Rufus'. Well, I suppose she would, would she not? So Rufus the Second has ascended our canine throne.

Our sadness at losing Rufus the First is assuaged, not only by his successor, but also by the coming of electricity to Vine's Farm. It is yet another expense we can do without, particularly on the back of having to pay Bingo Crouch. An unexpected benefactor, however, comes in the form of Clara, who reveals that she has been saving much of the regular payments she rightly receives for her share in the farming business.

"My needs are small," she declares. "I have food and a roof over my head. I always had it in mind I would pay for the electricity when it became available."

So now we are connected to the mains in time for Christmas, and we shall have much to celebrate.

Becky has settled in well as a boarder at Endacott Ladies' College. It was what she wanted, and I am relieved that she has no regrets. In one of her letters home, however, I see a problem looming. Riding stables have been established at the school, and the big boast on the latest prospectus is 'You can bring your own pony.' Needless to say, Becky wants a pony for Christmas. It is impossible. We cannot afford it, particularly with recently incurred expenditure.

I have to let her down gently, and I know my epistle to this effect will bring tears which I as an absent mother will not be able to mop up. I am left feeling I am a craven parent. Becky protests that, as we have a farm, keeping a pony during school holidays will not be a problem. She does not seem to comprehend that no matter where a pony is kept it devours money in addition to its purchase price.

I know that I shall find it even harder to justify our stance on the pony because the advent of electricity has inspired us to convert one of our bedrooms into a fully plumbed-in bathroom with available hot water. This really is modern civilised living for the household, but at a cost. It is Clara, however, who also finances this innovation.

"Before I die," she announces, "I want to know what it's like to live with convenience."

If I thought the pony issue was closed, then I am somewhat irked by its being resurrected. My daughter is nothing if not an artful little girl. It seems that she has a school friend by the name of Harriet. Harriet is from a wealthy family, and she too wants a pony. Her parents, however, live in London. I think I know where this is leading. Becky tells me that if Harriet's parents could find somewhere to keep a pony during the holidays, then Harriet could have a pony.

The two girls seem to have all this mapped out. Harriet's parents could buy their daughter a pony which could be stabled at Endacott during term time. In return for our agreeing to keep the pony here for the holidays, Becky would share use of the pony with Harriet at school and Harriet would be allowed to visit us at holiday time so the sharing arrangement could continue. Presumably, whenever Harriet is at home, Becky would have the pony all to herself. Do I detect another businesswoman emerging at such a tender age?

I write back and say that I should like to know what Harriet's parents think. I also point out that they would have to agree to reimburse us for the costs involved in keeping the pony here during the holidays. If I thought this would be the end of the matter, then I reckoned without Harriet's persuasive powers, which I suspect were honed through her association with my daughter.

Mr and Mrs Harrington-Scott would be delighted to placate their dear Harriet with the purchase of a pony if they could prevail upon our facilitating livery during vacations. Of course they would pay generously for this indulgence, and they say they consider it most efficacious that their daughter has found such a fine friend at school as Rebecca.

Well, I have to admit defeat. David and I invite Harriet and her parents to visit us during the Christmas holiday to inspect our stabling provision. We suggest using one of the vacant loose boxes at Vine's Farm. The Harrington-Scotts, however, are confident we shall take the very best care of any creature, and they decide a pony must be purchased immediately as their daughter's special early gift from Santa Claus!

So it comes to pass that, on the day autumn term finishes at Endacott College, Becky and Harriet are collected with their luggage and driven here in a Bentley behind which is a horsebox. On their arrival, the towed appendage is opened and out steps Clarence, a white gelding of little more than eleven hands, complete with halter. Also aboard is all manner of 'tack', as we now call it, including a beautifully crafted leather saddle which must have cost a fortune.

Clarence is led to his holiday accommodation, where Mr and Mrs Harrington-Scott enthuse as to its suitability. "How cosy he will be in his little house!" and "Look at that lovely straw all laid out for him!" are two comments which will live with me for quite some time. I point out that, although we have plenty of hay, we shall have to buy in oats as we have not grown that crop for some years. Under the circumstances we should be pleased to sow a small acreage from next year on land previously destined for a second wheat. This plan only goes to fuel our guests' delight.

Once Clarence has settled in with oats in his trough, a manger full of our best hay and a supply of water, we repair to the farmhouse, where I am heartily relieved that both bathroom and electricity have now been installed. I whisper to Becky not to reveal the recent arrival of these facilities, and not to provide details of privations hitherto experienced. It is only when Harriet's father asks for our telephone number that I realise our evolution into the twentieth century is not yet complete.

I explain that we intend to acquire this mode of communication in the new year as its usefulness to our business is a motivation complementary to our social requirements. I concede readily that progress in the countryside tends to lag somewhat behind life elsewhere – a humble submission which elicits a little polite sympathy from our metropolitan visitors.

It transpires that Harriet is an only child – a fact which I surmised in view of the apparent desire of her parents to accede to their daughter's wishes. If she is spoilt, however, I detect nothing but politeness from the girl. Indeed, she seems rather a reticent child and not one likely to throw a tantrum if she does not have her own way. I just hope that Becky does not try to take unfair advantage of her friend, and I make a mental note to remind my daughter of this when I am alone with her.

I gain further insight into the Harrington-Scott family when Harriet's mother confides in me that she had two miscarriages prior to giving birth to her daughter. I can well understand therefore why she and her husband might regard their offspring as somewhat precious. The fact that they have sent her to board at Endacott will perhaps be an advantage in that it should encourage Harriet to develop a sense of independence. I know it worked wonders for me while I was there.

The Harrington-Scotts are to stay with us for two days, after which they must leave so that we can accommodate Dotty and Henry, who will be joining us for Christmas. Harriet will have to double up with Becky.

Our loss of a bedroom to provide the new bathroom means that Lilian, who will also spend the festive season here, must sleep at Honeysuckle Cottage.

It is agreed that Harriet's family will depart after tea on the day my two old school friends arrive. This will enable our new acquaintances to meet Lilian, which they are very eager to do. They are mightily impressed that we know someone so famous

– a fact which mitigates any notion I may have that our dwelling and its environs must appear somewhat primitive in comparison to their address in Knightsbridge. Mr Harrington-Scott, we discover, is a barrister – a King's Counsel, no less – and we judge this does not compare favourably with the mucky business of keeping cows and delivering their milk on the doorstep. Do I detect an air of snobbishness somewhere which is not emanating from our London guests?

During his first year in office, Adolf Hitler has established a concentration camp in Southern Bavaria. It is called Dachau.

CHAPTER 22

OBSERVATIONS AND REFLECTIONS

The last of our wheat is threshed out by mid January 1934, and now we can assess what benefit has accrued through our return to arable cropping. The 120 Mill Farm acres sown during the autumn of 1932 and harvested last summer have yielded sixty-two tons of grain, thus averaging fractionally over ten hundredweight to the acre. At a 'standard price' of ten shillings per hundredweight under the terms of the Wheat Act we can expect a gross return of not less than £620. Of course this is not profit and we shall have to retain a little wheat for our poultry, but, set against the £750 we paid for the land and buildings at Mill Farm, I regard our progress as reasonably encouraging.

This puts into perspective the absurdly low price for which we acquired Mill Farm – a fact which when coupled with apparent inside information makes me feel almost guilty of fraud. All this is down to Henry, to whom David and I shall remain eternally grateful. It is, I suppose, just a case of being in the right place at the right time. We were the only prospective buyers – and reluctant ones at that – in a collapsed market where the vendor was desperate to dispose of the property.

How the fortunes of British agriculture have turned since the national government came into office and renounced free trade in favour of a little protectionism! It is a policy which flies in the face of modern thinking, and it may have serious ramifications for other industries, but at least there is some respite in the countryside. It has come too late for people like the Patemans and those who have racked up excessive debt in an attempt to ride out the storm. To others, however, who entered farming after land prices fell or, like ourselves, who reorganised and streamlined their activities to suit market conditions, there seems to be the possibility of a silver lining. Our Minister of Agriculture, Major Walter Elliot, who took up his present post during the autumn of 1932, is well thought of in farming circles. He is making a success of developing the agricultural marketing boards, of which the one for milk is central to our own business.

Seemingly motivated by renewed confidence in the milk industry, the dairy company in our local market town makes a fresh bid to buy our retailing enterprise. This is its first attempt in many years. No doubt our rivals are further encouraged by our recent purchase of Bingo Crouch's round. We are offered £300, which is increased to £350 when we refuse. When we tell them we should not even sell for £1,000 – a figure which it would be foolish to reject – we are troubled no longer.

The fact remains that milk production and retailing represent the core of our business, and we have expanded it to cover a wide area. It is profitable and made all the more attractive through the Milk Marketing Board.

We have a telephone installed at Vine's Farm and are assigned the number 19 from our small local exchange. I suppose this means that we are the nineteenth household to be connected in our community. Clara is suspicious of this apparatus coming into our home and, if she is honest, she would probably admit to being somewhat frightened by it. I try to nurture her confidence by encouraging her to speak to Becky whenever my daughter feels too lazy to write a letter and gleefully telephones us from school.

My son, James, is not allowed to telephone us without express permission from his headmaster, which is only granted in cases of emergency. James considers this most unfair as Becky is not similarly restricted provided she pays for the call out of her pocket money. I tell him that boys are being prepared for the world of work, where writing is an essential skill for advancement. Girls on the other hand may need to use the telephone if engaged in secretarial employment prior to marriage and, once married, may find the domestic telephone a useful adjunct to running the family home. James is not convinced and, although I refrain from telling him so, neither am I.

Notwithstanding the improvement in our farming finances, David and I are always on the lookout for innovations which might enhance our business. The episode with Clarence has set my thoughts racing towards the fact that, since we dispensed with shire horses in favour of a tractor, stabling at Vine's Farm, and for that matter at Mill Farm, has lain unused save for accommodating Clarence during school vacations.

We decide to let it be known that we should be pleased to provide livery facilities for anyone with a horse. David has it in mind to make our two Mill Farm employees responsible for this work as they are experienced carters who constantly bemoan the equine reduction on farms.

We doubt the response to our advertisements will be very great given the economic depression, yet we are pleasantly surprised to receive a few enquiries which result in four hunters coming to stay. We accommodate two at Vine's Farm and two next door. As well as providing us with additional income, they will be company for Clarence three times a year. In one of her telephone conversations Becky claims to be the inspiration for this enterprise and suggests it would be appropriate that she should receive some commission. My reply is unprintable!

My involvement in Bingo Crouch's old milk round takes me away from domestic duties, which puts unfair pressure on Clara. Somehow or other we manage, with Stella being an absolute brick in helping with household chores in addition to her duties in the dairy. I just do not know what we should do without Stella. How glad I am that we rescued her from her troubles in London!

The newly acquired milk round is somewhat arduous. Bingo's old van, despite its replacement track rod ends and other work performed on it by David, still looks a wreck. It scarcely enhances our business profile, but at least my new customers are used to it. Indeed, they seem to be pleased that I am their new 'milkman', and they often express words to the effect that I cut a more hygienic dash than my predecessor!

The vehicle is, however, appalling. My husband tells me it is not worth changing the oil because the engine burns so much that topping up the level is almost an oil change in itself. Clouds of blue smoke belch from the exhaust pipe, polluting the atmosphere, which I am sure does no good at all to the respiratory systems of any bystanders. Now in February there is still snow and ice about and the nearly bald tyres can hardly grip the road, particularly in this rather hilly district where I am constantly stopping and starting as I make my deliveries.

I tell David that despite the expense we really must do something about this situation. The two senior Model T vans are both more than twenty years old. Even our dear Lizzy is feeling her age. The time has come to trade in this pair of workhorses for something better. So we take delivery of two Ford Model A vans, one built in 1928, the other during the following year. At last we have vehicles with hand gear changes. Although I am consigned to our post-war Model T for what is the shortest milk round, I am nevertheless content because this particular vehicle was until now our best and the one David and I used as a surrogate car.

It is more than a year until James sits his Common Entrance Examination, the passing of which is necessary for him to gain admittance to my father's old public school (also attended by my brother, Edwin). The family is keen that my son should be educated there, not least because the ethos is more progressive than the traditionalism which so characterises most establishments. It seems to me that most boys' public schools are dedicated to providing the officer corps considered necessary to fight the next war. I do not want there to be another war, particularly in the wake of the recent carnage suffered between 1914 and 1918. I wish James to be prepared for entry into the profession of his choice. If he decides he would like to succeed us at Vine's Farm, then so be it, but I desire him to be well educated so that he will be able to farm from a position of intellectual strength rather than as a yokel with an inheritance.

I mention all this to Mr Claxton at Mill House, who delights me by offering to take James under his wing and to coach him during part of the school holidays. Of course it would only be right to pay our neighbour for his services, and this would be an additional burden which we can ill afford now that two of the vans have been replaced. The matter is resolved when Mr and Mrs Claxton tell me they would be more than happy to be paid in milk, eggs and potatoes. So the barter system is resurrected and comes to our rescue.

As weeks pass the acquisition of electricity spawns further aids to relieve domestic drudgery. We now have an electric iron and a vacuum cleaner. My extra duties delivering milk are the excuse for these purchases. On the debit side, however, I find myself frequently tripping over a flex whenever it is my turn to vacuum the carpets. It seems that every advantage is tempered by a disadvantage. Even if labour-saving devices could be used without potential hazards, there will always be the purchase cost and the feared prospect of technical failure.

One innovation we have so far resisted is a wireless. There is much speculation that this intrusion into people's homes threatens the very existence of newspapers and might even extinguish conversation. A scenario is envisaged whereby families throughout the land will sit silently, staring into space, while the British Broadcasting Corporation controls all incoming thought.

Also predicted is the demise of the household piano. Why should one undergo the onerous task of learning to play this instrument when one can summon a forty-piece orchestra at the turn of a knob? I arrest this anticipated development through teaching Becky to read music and to play the upright piano in our parlour. Further lessons are arranged for her at Endacott. I do wonder, however, whether my daughter might be the last of the Coulthursts to make her own music.

The four liveried horses placed in our charge are turned out to pasture in the spring, although they are returned to their stables each night. The largest hunter is a twelve-year-old mare in excess of sixteen hands. Despite her maturity, a young stallion has taken a fancy to her. I observe him one day trying to mount the object of his desire. This is unrequited love, however, and the mare rejects his advances by urinating over him. What a mercy it is that we human ladies do not have to fend off men in like manner!

During the last three years the cost-cutting national government has been operating a 'means test' on long-term-unemployed persons who have exhausted their National Insurance contributions and are receiving financial relief in the form of 'transitional benefit'. Administration of this system is devolved to Public Assistance Committees of local councils whose decisions vary in different parts of the country. This of course leads to inequity.

The means test is a most hated entity whereby a claimant may have to sell possessions deemed unnecessary before assistance is forthcoming. Now, in 1934, the Chancellor of the Exchequer, Neville Chamberlain, inspires an Unemployment Act under which a statutory committee is set up to run unemployment insurance nationwide with a fund designed to break even at the current unemployment rate of sixteen and three-quarters per cent. This seemingly welcome move, however, does not abolish the means test, which remains a bone of contention. The Act renames 'benefit' as 'assistance' and creates the Unemployment Assistance Board, under which new national rates of payment to the unemployed are to be introduced next January.

As I read of these developments in the newspapers I am conscious of the fact that Britain is still in the economic doldrums. It would be easy for me to think that all is well because agriculture has been given something of a lift, albeit from a very low base. In truth, an unemployment rate in excess of sixteen per cent is horrendous and causes much misery in our industrial areas.

Even in farming there continues to be distress as so much capital has been lost through devaluation of land bought on mortgage when prices were high. At Vine's Farm we are also victims of this phenomenon, but our position has been eased by retailing some of our produce and receiving injections of cash from family sources. The acquisition of Mill Farm at absurdly low cost has also been a boon to our prospects. So we are lucky despite our struggles, and we must be thankful.

There has been, however, one problem brewing in our business for too long. It relates to the two workers we inherited from Mill Farm. Though experienced and able, they refuse to accept that tractors are the inevitable future of farming. Ultimately the shire horse will be superseded and consigned to the history books. These men cannot drive Beatrice, our solitary tractor, and their unwillingness to learn is affecting efficiency.

David spends too many hours operating our sole source of motive power in the fields, and he only ever gets relieved by Bill or Frank when they have finished their milk rounds. This is not fair and it has got to stop. Moreover, if we ever buy a second tractor – and we could certainly do with one – it would be unacceptable to have it standing idle for any part of the day while we are busy with field work.

David therefore issues an ultimatum. At least one of these two men must learn to drive Beatrice or find a job elsewhere – presumably where horses are still used. My husband's initiative is not well received and it results in both labourers handing in their notices. We are surprised they have found new positions at their ages, particularly as they require tied cottages with their new employment. Within a fortnight, however, they are gone, so David and I are landed with the extra burden of caring for the liveried horses.

This awkward situation cannot be allowed to continue for long, but it nevertheless does provide an opportunity. Our two erstwhile employees occupied a pair of semi-detached cottages which came with Mill Farm when we bought it. This, of course, makes the farm look all the cheaper, but these dwellings are in poor condition and coming to the end of their useful lives. What to do about this is answered by Bill, who lets it be known that he would like to become a full-time farmworker and says that he can easily find another van driver who would not require a tied cottage.

David and I breathe huge sighs of relief, especially when Bill agrees to learn to look after the liveried horses. So, on Bill's recommendation, we engage a young man called Jack, who is trained to discharge milk-round duties. Hence the way is paved for us to sell the two vacant cottages, which could with advantage be demolished and a new single dwelling erected in their stead. A purchaser is found with precisely this plan in mind. The sale realises £350, which enables us to buy that much needed second tractor with cash to spare. This time we obtain a second-hand

Fordson with rubber tyres, which can thus be driven along public roads.

Bill is enjoying his new role. Although of a more mechanical bent, he has proved adept in his equine duties. Becky and Harriet are particularly happy that he is also caring for Clarence during the school holidays. Now a family man, Bill presents a friendly disposition towards children; and the two girls love to visit his cottage to see baby Keith, who will reach his second birthday in August.

Some of the surplus cash raised from selling the squalid Mill Farm cottages is invested in further household appliances. We have bought an electric cooker and two portable electric fires. I have noticed how Clara has become somewhat slower recently; and it is an advantage for her not to have to struggle with the kitchen range, which has been in our house since Victorian times. The range, however, remains in situ in case of power cuts. The electric fires are purchased with bedrooms in mind. How I hate emerging from my warm bed on a winter's morning to shiver while washing and dressing and being reminded of the cold by icicles stuck to the inside of the windowpanes!

We weaken further before summer is upon us – we buy a wireless. Again we have Clara in our thoughts because she is often left alone in the house when Stella, David and I are working and the children are at school. Anyway, that is my excuse for the wooden box in one corner of the parlour. When reception is poor it blows raspberries at us, the attempted cure for which is a smart rap on its top from David. Sometimes his unscientific remedy actually works!

Lilian has a refrigerator in her London flat. Can you imagine? Domestic electricity has given rise to all manner of inventions and I cannot think where it will all end.

In late June Adolf Hitler acts against leaders of the Nazi storm troopers and other political opponents. Seventy-seven men are executed on charges of treason. People call this event 'the night of the long knives'. The storm troopers are then absorbed into the German army and all personnel of the united force are obliged to swear an oath of allegiance to the Führer. On 2 July the *Daily*

Mail publishes an article which commends these happenings. I am shown a copy by one of my milk customers. It reads, 'Herr Adolf Hitler, the German Chancellor, has saved his country.' It goes on to say, 'Hitler's love of Germany has triumphed over private friendships and fidelity to comrades who had stood shoulder to shoulder with him in the fight for Germany's future.'

I wonder.

CHAPTER 23

CONSIDERATIONS AND CALAMITIES

In 1935 my son, James, passes his Common Entrance Examination, much to the relief of David and me. Now he can follow in the scholarly footsteps of his grandfather and uncle. We say a very big thank you to Mr Claxton next door, who has been a most patient, able tutor and without whom my son's passage to the school of our choice might have been a more hazardous one.

Becky will be spared a similar experience at Endacott, where admittance to the senior school is automatic for any pupil schooled in the junior department. The assumption seems to be that any girl educated in the latter is clearly high-class material for the rigours to be experienced later. James just thinks that girls get away with it!

My husband and I nevertheless monitor Becky's progress. We are not going to tolerate her schooldays being an ongoing holiday with the added attraction of riding Clarence through the agreeable Sussex countryside.

The first field of oats destined for Clarence and the other liveried horses is growing apace and provides one crop not dependent upon the vagaries of market forces. That is the beauty of any crop consumed on the farm.

With two tractors operational and clement weather last autumn, all our white straw crops were sown by the close of October. This is most satisfactory as our heavy clay soil lies wet once autumnal rains start in earnest. Spring-sown cereals never yield as well as those drilled earlier, particularly if seasonal rainfall is low as often is the case in South East England.

On 6 May 1935 King George V celebrates his silver jubilee and rides in an open carriage with Queen Mary through the streets of London. I sometimes wonder whether these events are orchestrated to divert public attention away from the socio-economic ills of our country. Perhaps I am just being cynical, but, despite improvements since the dark days of 1931, there are still one and a half million people unemployed.

On 7 June Ramsay MacDonald and Stanley Baldwin exchange roles in the national government. Mr MacDonald's health is failing, so he becomes Lord President of the Council while Mr Baldwin becomes Prime Minister for the third time.

There has been much debate of late on the subject of defence. The question is whether to rearm. The government is in favour, but the disarmament lobby is determined to be heard. The League of Nations Union goes to the length of organising a house-to-house canvass. The results are made known on 28 June. Over eleven and a half million people have responded. There is a ringing endorsement for collective security by any method other than war, with a more hesitant support for an aggressor to be halted by war.

On 3 October Italy, under its fascist dictator, Benito Mussolini, attacks Abyssinia. The League of Nations applies economic sanctions against the invader, thus responding through collective security in line with opinions expressed in the house-to-house canvass.

It cannot be long before a British general election is held. The national government has been in power since 1931, and there are clear signs that preparations are being made. When new rates of unemployment assistance began in January they turned out in many cases to be lower than those awarded by erstwhile local Public Assistance Committees, particularly in the most distressed areas. Public demonstrations and hunger marches ensued, which prompted the government to intervene through preventing any reductions in the previous rates. I question whether this intervention would have occurred if a general election were not in the offing.

Now that the government is in something of a dilemma

over rearmament it hatches a plan to resolve the difficulty. An announcement is made giving full support for collective security provided all other members of the League of Nations are similarly disposed. The theory seems to be that if collective security works, then the national government can take the credit. This principle could be applied against Nazi-led Germany, which is now being seen as the greatest danger to peace. If the plan fails, then other member states could be held culpable and Britain would be justified in rearming.

Having positioned itself nicely, it is hardly surprising the government dissolves Parliament on 25 October. Polling day is set for 14 November.

My husband has always teased me about my interest in current affairs whenever he sees my head buried in one of my father's cast-off newspapers. Now that we have a wireless the two of us sit in silence as we listen to the nine-o'clock evening news bulletin. David's understanding of worldly matters has been acquired from information gleaned from this source, and we find ourselves discussing issues which hitherto were scarcely a topic of conversation.

Clara's analysis of events beyond our local community is that what will happen will happen no matter what anyone thinks at Vine's Farm. She is probably right, but I do not wish my mind to be restricted to milk bottles and egg boxes. Stella, who usually sits with us in the evenings, regards our farm as a sanctuary from a desperately unhappy world, and she speaks with authority.

James started boarding at his new school in September, and his letters home indicate that he has settled in well. It seems that several of his contemporaries also have family connections with the institution, which bodes well, I think. James is old for his year and he will celebrate his fourteenth birthday on 7 November.

A week after this anniversary Clara, David and I enter the village hall to cast our votes in the general election. The campaign leading up to polling day has been dominated by issues such as unemployment and housing rather than foreign policy and rearmament. Understandably I suppose, in view of the depression, people are more concerned with matters at home.

One hundred and fifty-four Labour candidates opposed to the national government are elected – an increase of over 100. National Labour suffers losses to the extent that Ramsay MacDonald loses his seat! Non-national Liberals are reduced to just twenty seats. The national government emerges victorious with 432 members returned. As the economic sanctions applied against Italy have not worked, the government now has a mandate for rearmament.

In late November I receive word that the Countess of Cloudsley has died. I write a letter of condolence to the 5th Earl and I am surprised to be invited to a tea at Cloudsley Hall, arranged to follow the funeral. The invitation extends to my husband. On the appointed day our parish church is packed, and many villagers are left outside, unable to gain access. The Cloudsley family has always taken a paternalistic approach towards the local community, and a mutual respect has developed over several generations. It does now look, however, as though we are nearing the end of an era. The Earl's only son was killed in the Great War, and his two daughters are married and living in London. The Earl himself is now an octogenarian and it seems only a question of time before Cloudsley Hall falls into a stranger's hands.

My prognosis proves to be more true than I could have imagined, for Lord Cloudsley tells me during the funeral tea that he will be selling up almost immediately and decamping to the capital to be nearer his daughters.

"I should just rattle around this great house on my own, Mrs Coulthurst, with only the servants for company. I'm far too old to have new aspirations."

"We shall all miss you, My Lord."

"Yes, absolutely," echoes David.

His Lordship tries to fashion a smile. "Well, I shall miss everyone here too," he confesses. "But I'm a victim of old age and I really don't have the energy or even the land to be a country squire any more. I am glad to meet you both here though. You've made a real go of things at Vine's Farm despite all the difficulties with agriculture in recent years."

"We couldn't have done it without you," admits David.

Lord Cloudsley chuckles briefly.

"You've got your wife to thank for that, young man. She twisted me round her little finger – didn't you, my dear?"

I blush with embarrassment.

Our host introduces us to his daughters and their husbands. There ensues much talk about Endacott, for we are three old girls of this establishment. My two seniors are fascinated to learn of the latest facilities enjoyed by Becky. They can scarcely believe that one is permitted to bring one's own pony to school and have it stabled there.

"Things were very strict in our day," advises Lady Clarissa.

"Rather like a female army battalion," suggests Lady Constance.

I think they are exaggerating, although they did leave Endacott several years prior to my arrival.

The advent of the telephone at Vine's Farm has caused a marked reduction in correspondence. I used to look forward to receiving letters from Dotty and Lilian. Now, whenever they wish to communicate, they ring me up. Of course it is pleasant to hear their voices, but I do wonder whether good letter writing is a skill which will become more honoured in the breach than in the observance.

Christmas comes and goes and we progress into 1936. The year does not start well for Britain as the death of King George V is announced on 20 January. The Prince of Wales ascends to the throne as King Edward VIII. He is over forty and not yet married, although he is no stranger to the company of women.

Lord Cloudsley has moved to London and the house and grounds of Cloudsley Hall have been sold. The new owner is a remote figure who spends much of his time away from the community. He is clearly a wealthy man, and rumours abound that he was a war profiteer.

On 7 March German troops occupy the demilitarised Rhineland. The French do nothing to oppose them. Our own country follows suit. The League of Nations declares that

Germany has broken the Treaties of Versailles and Locarno, but does not even impose economic sanctions against the perpetrator. Adolf Hitler – the German dictator, as we can now properly call him – is invited to negotiate a new arrangement for European security. He responds by stating that he has 'no territorial claims in Europe' and proposes a non-aggression pact with Western powers. The national government in Britain seeks clarification by submitting a list of questions. Hitler does not reply. How can one do diplomatic business with such a man?

David and I receive a letter from the deputy headmistress of Endacott College. I open it with a little trepidation, fearing that Becky has blotted her copybook in some way. I am relieved to learn that a collection is being taken up for Miss Buckmaster, who is to retire at the end of the summer term. As parents we are invited to contribute. We send £2, which we could well do with ourselves; but I expect many donations will be far in excess of this, and we do not wish to appear mean. Apparently there is to be a surprise presentation on the last day of the school year, which all parents are welcome to attend. It is agreed that I at least should attend to support our daughter.

Fascism, alas, is not the preserve of just Germany and Italy. We have the British Union of Fascists (BUF) founded by Oswald Mosley. This would-be messiah of British politics could be construed as a false prophet, having shifted from the Conservatives to Labour to his own New Party and now to the BUF. In accord with fascist tradition, Mosley's followers rely on marches and violence to achieve their ends rather than meetings and debate. They are often referred to as 'blackshirts', owing to their uniforms. Their behaviour now has become so appalling that the government passes a Public Order Act prohibiting all political uniforms and giving the police power to ban political processions. Thank goodness! It has been said of Mosley that he is a politician in a hurry. I believe that if he runs fast enough, he will trip himself up and fall flat on his face.

199

Our village windmill has just closed. Improved road transport has rendered it uneconomic to grind corn in nearly every parish for local use. Our miller's retirement has sounded the death knell, and the four sails of our mill will rotate no longer. The flour of our youth is dead and turned to a more permanent form of dust!

Progress – particularly technical progress – is advancing at such a rate that I can hardly keep pace with it. As November approaches, both Dotty and Lilian inform me by telephone that they have purchased television receivers. The BBC is to broadcast monochrome pictures as well as sound into domestic premises from 2 November. Reception is only possible within a fifteen-mile radius of Alexandra Palace – not that David and I could contemplate owning such a new plaything. Indeed, this innovation is only for the wealthy as receivers are very expensive.

Talking of palaces, we learn that the Crystal Palace has burnt down. Apparently the fire was so fierce that its glow could be seen from as far away as Brighton. This fine glass structure was built to house the Great Exhibition at Hyde Park in 1851. It was moved to Sydenham three years later and had been standing there ever since. A part of our heritage has been consigned to history. What a shame!

On 2 December a bombshell is exploded by the national newspapers. Our king wishes to marry a twice-divorced American lady by the name of Wallace Simpson. This desire, it seems, is vehemently opposed by the British establishment and the Dominions to the extent that even a morganatic union is deemed unacceptable. Despite efforts from some quarters to support His Majesty, the King abdicates on 11 December, broadcasting his decision to the nation on the wireless. David and I listen intently to his parting words, and we opine that the whole business seems to have been concluded with indecent haste. The former Edward VIII leaves the country that evening and he is replaced by his younger brother, the Duke of York, who becomes King George VI.

Two days later the Archbishop of Canterbury, Cosmo Gordon

Lang, delivers a character assassination of the erstwhile monarch over the airwaves, claiming that 'he stands rebuked by the nation'. So acerbic is the prelate's address that we are left in little doubt that he was a participatory architect in this sorry affair and that perhaps it is he who should be rebuked by the nation.

1936 has been an eventful year, and one which, in part at least, I am happy to forget.

CHAPTER 24

PRIDE, LOSS AND PESSIMISM

In the spring of 1937 the post-war Model T van, which I use to deliver milk, begins to give trouble. A leaking head gasket is diagnosed by David and we have to decide whether to pay for an expensive repair or replace the ailing vehicle.

Our finances are stretched, but we resolve to bite the bullet and trade in the last of our Model Ts for a Ford van of the type which is still in current production. Thus we take delivery of a two-year-old Model Y, which I rather selfishly bag for my own use. My argument is that this new acquisition will double up as social transport for my husband and me. The purchase of a car remains quite beyond our pocket. The interests of the farm have to take precedence.

I am therefore feeling a little self-satisfied as I go about my milk round, displaying the pride which so often precedes a fall. The fall manifests itself in the form of a puncture – remarkably, the first one I have experienced since that wet day many years ago when Lizzy almost broke my thumb with her starting handle.

I try to take a pragmatic view and remain calm. David has shown me that tools, including the starting handle, are accommodated in the engine compartment. With an air of mechanical competence I lift the bonnet and open the wooden toolbox only to find there is no wheel brace inside. My aura of placidity is at first threatened and then assaulted as a few beads of perspiration upon my brow begin to induce a feeling of blind panic.

Words which do not form part of my regular vocabulary fill

my mind, yet mercifully I restrain myself from blurting them out at an unchecked volume. I try to retain outward serenity, telling myself that there must be some logical explanation for my predicament. David is mechanically minded and I know he inspected the van thoroughly before I ventured forth in it. I stare at the contents of the toolbox and then cast my eyes about the engine compartment. Clipped on to the rear bulkhead is the starting handle – an instrument which I am relieved not to need because the vehicle has a self-starter and the battery is well charged. My eyes, however, remain fixed upon the handle for a reason which soon becomes apparent. At the end of its crank is located a female hexagon designed to fit a nut. Perhaps I should have realised that a man obsessed with reducing production costs like Henry Ford would supply one tool capable of performing more than one task.

Eureka! The wheel brace is incorporated in the starting handle. In a moment of self-exoneration I feel I could brain David for not bringing this fact to my notice. I resolve, however, not to mention the matter as he would almost certainly tell me that any reasonably intelligent person should be able to work it out for himself, or even *her*self.

My troubles, however, are not over. Try as I may I cannot loosen the wheel nuts. I parody the words of Queen Elizabeth: "I know I have the body of a weak and feeble woman, but I have the heart and stomach of someone who is going to undo these bloody wheel nuts!"

In a fit of inspiration I recall seeing a hammer in the toolbox, so I commandeer it for the purpose of hitting the starting handle in an attempt to shock the nuts loose. The plan fails, and I am just about to succumb to that female trait of bursting into tears when an aged labourer, leading a shire horse and tumbrel laden with mangolds, comes into view. I have no option but to seek his assistance.

His rustic appearance is indicative of one who acquired his adult image before the turn of the century: leather boots and gaiters, a waistcoat from which hangs a watch chain, and a droopy moustache, all topped off with a cloth cap. He stops to assess my situation, and I guess, in mortification, I shall have to endure a diatribe on the folly of trying to replace the horse with the internal combustion engine.

My bucolic knight in not so shining armour does not disappoint. He reminds me that a horse discharges dung most efficacious to the health of roses while the motor vehicle discharges nothing but poisonous fumes. He reminds me further that equine shoes do not have punctures – an observation which feels painfully apposite in the prevailing circumstances.

In the fullness of time my saviour turns his attention to the business in hand, and, with irritatingly little effort, succeeds in slackening my van's wheel nuts.

"You can jack 'er up now, missus," he advises.

I try to reward him financially, but he will not hear of it.

"May I at least offer you a bottle of milk?"

Reluctantly he accepts, removes the cardboard top and puts the bottle to his lips. Having drunk the entire contents, he wipes his sleeve across his mouth and hands me the empty bottle.

"Ar, that's one thing progress can't change," he remarks. "Milk's always come from a cow, and that's how it's always going to be."

He offers to help me further, but I tell him that I can now manage and I thank him for his trouble. He trudges onwards with his mangolds while I set about changing the wheel. The spare one is strapped to the outside of the nearside door, there being no room to accommodate it inside with all the eggs and crates of milk. I complete the task without further difficulty and don my white coat, which I had removed to prevent it becoming grubby.

Despite the delay, I finish my round without receiving any customer complaints. On the return journey I experience the familiar musical accompaniment of empty milk bottles jangling in their crates as the van negotiates the narrow, winding lanes.

Upon arrival at Vine's Farm it occurs to me that no matter how I try to conceal this episode from my husband, the story will get back to him via the bush telegraph. Nearly everybody seems to know everyone else's business in our rural community.

On 12 May King George VI is crowned in Westminster Abbey by Archbishop Lang, who left a rather nasty taste in many mouths with his denunciation of Edward VIII. Shortly afterwards the Prime Minister, Stanley Baldwin, retires from the House of Commons and is created an earl. Ramsay MacDonald, having returned to Parliament in a by-election, retires at the same time yet accepts no honour. The Chancellor of the Exchequer, Neville Chamberlain, becomes Prime Minister and Sir John Simon takes over at the Treasury.

In July a special telephone number is created in London for anyone needing to contact the emergency services. The number is easy to remember: 999. In the event of this facility being extended nationwide, I educate James and Becky never to abuse it.

I am pleased to say that Becky and Harriet have forged a friendship which has stood the test of time. Clarence, the pony which did so much to cement their association, has been replaced by a larger steed to take account of the needs of two growing girls. There were tears when Clarence was taken away to provide for a younger owner, but now we have Eddie, a thirteen-hands-high gelding who, like his predecessor, is liveried here during school holidays. I explain to both girls, as I am sure Harriet's parents have already done, that it has to be this way when a rider has outgrown her mount although it is always difficult to say farewell to an old friend. I point out that, in their lifetimes, there will be occasions when one has to say goodbye, and this event is part of their training for adulthood.

David and I now count Mr and Mrs Harrington-Scott, or Tarquin and Isabelle, amongst our friends. We see them regularly, six times a year, when they come to transport Becky, Harriet and now Eddie to and from Endacott.

The Chamberlain government has adopted a policy of appeasement in relation to the rise of fascism in Europe.

Evidence for the folly of this approach arises this summer when British, French and Russian merchant ships carrying food and civilian supplies to Spain are sunk by unidentified submarines in the Mediterranean. The location of these outrages suggests that Italy is the likeliest culprit. The Spanish republic has been fighting a civil war against the fascists of General Franco since last July. It is known that both Germany and the Italians are intervening in this conflict to Franco's advantage. Only now do Britain and France act by forming anti-submarine patrols. The sinkings cease. If this is not clear evidence that standing up to fascism through collective security is a successful policy, then I fail to understand what is. The lesson, however, is not learnt and Franco continues to enjoy the support of Hitler and Mussolini.

One Sunday in October, with the children away at school, Clara, Stella, David and I are having a roast lunch at Vine's Farm. We are in good spirits and, with dessert consumed, we look forward to putting our feet up with a cup of tea once the dishes are washed. Although busily engaged in conversation, I begin to notice a vacant expression forming on Clara's face. Within a few seconds her head falls to one side and she slumps in her chair. The room is silent momentarily.

"David," I say with more than an air of concern, "her cheeks are turning blue."

Scarcely knowing what to do next, we ease Clara on to the thick rug by the fireplace and support her head with a cushion. David and I stare at each other while Stella is visibly upset. I try to feel Clara's pulse and detect nothing. There is no obvious evidence of her breathing.

"Darling," I confess to my husband, "I fear she is dead."

David looks distraught.

"How can she be? She was talking only a minute or so ago. She ate everything on her plate and said how good it was."

I take David's hand and then kiss him gently.

"We have to call the doctor," I advise.

"Shall I do it, Vera?" offers Stella.

"Oh, yes, would you, please?"

Stella goes to the telephone in the hall and returns shortly.

"He's coming right away."

I force a smile in gratitude.

"Shouldn't we ask for an ambulance?" protests David.

"Darling, I really think it's too late for that. Surely you can see. I'm so sorry."

"I don't understand."

"No," I sympathise, "there's so much in this world that's too difficult to understand."

I realise, of course, that this situation is far more traumatic for my husband than it is for me. Notwithstanding the death and filth he must have experienced on the Western Front, Clara was his mother and the last living link with his early life.

The local doctor arrives in his car and soon pronounces Clara as having passed away.

"I should say it was a cerebral haemorrhage," he remarks. "If it's any consolation, I can think of few better ways to go. I know it must be a shock to you, but she didn't suffer. I'll make out the necessary certificate. The village policeman will probably want to take details from you later on. You will, of course, need to make the necessary arrangements with a funeral director for removal of the body as soon as possible. As it's Sunday I can give you a number to ring if that's any help."

Clara is taken away that afternoon. We are numb from these events. I tell David to sit in the parlour while Stella and I attend to the washing-up resulting from lunch. He refuses and insists on drying the wet items.

"Life has to go on," he asserts. "I saw plenty of death in the war, so I ought to be able to cope with this. It's better to do something rather than just mope."

The local police constable arrives on his bicycle and we relate matters to him. He takes notes, expresses condolences and rides away.

I am relieved that James and Becky were not here. It is not going to be easy for them to deal with the loss of their grandmother, with whom they have lived since their births. That evening I telephone their schools and explain everything. It is not a pleasant task for any mother.

David tells me that Clara was seventy-five. What changes she saw in her lifetime! When she was born there were no motor cars or aeroplanes, no electric light, no films or wireless, yet now Lilian and Dotty have television receivers! I am just glad that in her declining years she was able to experience some of the modern conveniences many of us are inclined to take for granted.

Within a week the funeral is held in the parish church where David and I were married more than eighteen years ago. Clara is buried in the churchyard between her late husband and elder son, Vere, who was killed in France. James and Becky each expressed a wish to attend the ceremony. They were both given three days off from school so that no travelling was necessary on the day of the service. My parents collected them by car yesterday and will return them tomorrow. James has remained stoic, but Becky is almost beyond consolation. Her grandmother was always strict with her yet scrupulously fair and supportive. It is as though a rock of guidance and example has been removed from the foundation of Becky's life. She will have to be strong.

In November the weakness of the League of Nations is exposed.

Japan has been an aggressor towards China ever since Manchuria was occupied six years ago. Now the Japanese have renewed the fighting and China has appealed to the League in Geneva. The League, however, has acted pusillanimously through referring the matter to a conference convened in Brussels by nine countries. Britain offers to support any action in which the United States is prepared to participate. The problem is that America enjoys a profitable trading relationship with Japan and so nothing is done. All the conference does is to register its disapproval before dispersing. Hence the doctrine of collective security is once again abandoned. I just hope the world is not sleepwalking into another major conflict.

I admit to becoming more than a little depressed not only by international matters, but also by those closer to home. When people die one tends to measure their importance by the gap they leave in our own lives. I now realise how significant Clara was at Vine's Farm. I notice her absence whenever I enter the farmhouse. All the domestic work she did within its walls seemed to be completed automatically. We did not notice it because we did not see it being done while we were going about our farming duties. Now we notice these things because they are not done unless we do them ourselves.

I am so relieved we have Stella here. Without her, David and I should feel this house is too big for us, particularly when the children are away at school. I cannot imagine having to do all the housework myself in addition to delivering milk and eggs. Stella is marvellous. Although she must be tired from her duties in the dairy, with two milkings per day, she busies herself in the house to the extent that she is an inspiration. David – bless him – is also a fine example by helping with washing-up and any other household chores which might otherwise be left undone.

The blunt truth is that we cannot afford to hire any further domestic help. Despite government policies which have assisted agriculture in recent years, our margins are small and each expense we incur has to be justified on the grounds of essentiality.

Owing to my feelings of loss and fatigue I try to cheer myself up by inviting Lilian, Dotty and Henry for Christmas. With the children home too it should make for a much needed happy time, even without Clara. In this plan, however, I am thwarted, for Lilian has begun a new play in the West End and Dotty has arranged to visit her parents with her husband. So I sink into a new abyss of dissatisfaction until I think, albeit pessimistically, of inviting Tarquin and Isabelle Harrington-Scott. I say 'pessimistically' because I have little doubt they have a thousand better things to do than decamp to a rather shabby farmhouse in the rustic environs of deepest Sussex.

Imagine my elation, therefore, when they tell me they have yet to make any definite plans and would be delighted to accept. This means that Becky and Harriet will be together during the holiday and will no doubt enjoy the company of Eddie.

In the event, we all have a wonderful festive period. Secretly I am amazed at how Isabelle has adapted to the work ethic within our dwelling. I know she has three servants at home and spends much of her life socialising or raising money for charity, yet she refuses to let herself be waited upon and gives me the impression that she views domestic activity as something of an adventure!

CHAPTER 25

ON THE BRINK

My depressed spirits of autumn are sadly rekindled in the new year. Adolf Hitler has forced the Austrian Chancellor to resign after demanding that he should admit Nazis into his Cabinet. What business is it of Hitler's to interfere with the politics of another country? The new Chancellor, who is pro-Nazi, now invites German troops to enter Austria on the ridiculous pretext of restoring law and order!

Needless to say this is an orchestrated opportunity which the Führer cannot resist. On 13 March 1938 the Germans cross the border without encountering any opposition. Hitler rides through the streets of Vienna to cheering crowds, and Austria is annexed to Germany. This process is known as the Anschluss, or connection. I find it difficult to believe, however, that all Austrians are happy with this state of affairs. It may be a bloodless coup, but it leaves an unpleasant taste in my mouth and a feeling which does not augur well for the future.

On the following day Winston Churchill, so long frozen out of government, warns the House of Commons that Europe is confronted with an aggressive programme by the Nazis which has not yet run its course. The question is who will be next on the list? With three million Germans living in Czechoslovakia, one might hazard an intelligent guess.

A farmer's wife in Sussex, however, has no say in these events. A cobbler must stick to his last, and I must stick to my milk round and matters domestic. Spring has now sprung, the cows are yielding well, the hens are laying well and the fields are flush with grass and corn. Our own little corner of England is fecund and at peace in an uncertain world. Hedgerows and trees, too, stand verdant in the wake of their winter defoliation.

In June the mower cuts the grass laid up for conservation and hay is made. Having finished my milk round for the day, I temporarily abandon farmhouse duties and take beer to the men sweating with pitchforks as wagons are laden with the sweet-scented crop. Thus is slaked the thirst of David and Bill, and also Frank and Jack, who, like me, have completed their milk deliveries.

In August the children are home and Harriet is staying with us. The wheat fields are a hive of activity as we put sheaves into stooks. Everyone lends a hand, and we consume picnics and engage in laughter even as we work. Eddie, very much a non-labouring horse, stands dutifully beside Harriet and Becky, content with his nosebag for he has nothing to graze in the stubble beneath his hooves. Rufus the Second, our golden cocker spaniel, runs about the field with his nose to the ground and his tail wagging in expectation of finding a rabbit to chase or anything else he deems interesting.

The harvest, however, is not yet complete when in early September rumblings of discontent emanate from Czechoslovakia. On the 4th of the month President Beneš agrees to all the demands made by Germans living in his country. Nine days later they attempt a revolt, which is put down. France, allied to the Czechs, fears a German invasion, but is reluctant to act and instead gives our Prime Minister a free hand to address German grievances. Hence Neville Chamberlain flies to Munich on the 15th and meets Adolf Hitler. They agree to separate the Germans living in the Sudetenland from the remainder of Czechoslovakia. There follows an argument with the French which results in President Beneš assenting to the separation on the 21st, having been given an ultimatum that otherwise Britain and France would not come to his defence if attacked by Germany.

The following day Mr Chamberlain flies again to see Hitler, only to learn that the Führer is demanding immediate occupation of the Sudetenland by German troops. When the

Prime Minister returns home he is met with such opposition that Britain begins war preparations. Trenches are dug in London parks and anti-aircraft guns deployed. Air-raid sirens are tried out on the wireless and gas masks are delivered to regional centres. The nation holds its breath and grows ever more apprehensive.

Parliament is recalled and Mr Chamberlain announces on 28 September that Hitler has agreed to a conference at Munich to include France and Italy. The Prime Minister yet again flies to Germany the next day. An agreement is reached allowing that the Sudetenland be occupied over a period of ten days. It is also agreed that the remainder of Czechoslovakia should be guaranteed by the four powers once the question of Hungarian and Polish minorities there is settled.

The Prime Minister returns to Britain the following day. Emerging from his aircraft at Heston Aerodrome, he waves a piece of paper bearing Herr Hitler's signature to the effect that our two peoples desire never to go to war with one another again. In the evening he appears at a window of 10 Downing Street to address the cheering crowd below. He declares that he believes "It is peace for our time."

I tell David how relieved I am, but my husband is less than sanguine.

"I don't want to distress you, darling," he responds; "but if Chamberlain has done us any favour, he has just bought us more time to rearm."

My heart sinks.

"Do you think war is inevitable, then?"

"Put it this way: I believe what Churchill is telling us. Hitler's plan is to take what he wants when he wants it. He will pick off countries one by one until someone stops him by threat of force or even by force itself. This Hitler is a disease that's bound to flourish when a defeated nation is driven down by victors' justice and economic slump. A people without hope will follow anyone who promises this and promises that and who can lift expectations from a soapbox. It could have happened here with a man like Mosley, but it didn't because we're a little more sceptical in Britain and our democracy is sound. The League of Nations is a washout. First Abyssinia, then the Rhineland, then China, then Austria and now the Sudetenland. Can you see any end to it?"

I am beginning to wish I had not said anything. Owing to his war experiences, David tends to be cynical about such matters; yet I detect a chilling logic in his argument and feel compelled to question him further.

"So who do you think will become the next victim?"

"I don't know, but I can give you a list of countries which look vulnerable. It all depends on whether you see the aggressor as Germany, Italy or Japan. In my view Germany poses the greatest threat at the moment, so one might guess the remainder of Czechoslovakia. One country I've always thought unsafe is Poland. Didn't anyone at Versailles have the wit to realise that cutting East Prussia off from the rest of Germany was a recipe for future conflict? How should we have reacted in similar circumstances? A nation should never be divided from itself."

My depressed thoughts about current affairs are soon diverted to more mundane matters. Our dairyman, George Akehurst, lets it be known that he wishes to retire. Dear old George, he has worked on this farm since he was a boy, and that is more than sixty years ago. He has been a fixture here for so long that we have come to regard him as ageless. Anno Domini, however, catches up with all of us, and George is past his three score years and ten. It is remarkable that a man of such advanced age has managed to keep going; but if anyone deserves a happy retirement, then it is he.

George is worried about the position with regard to his tied cottage. So many agricultural labourers in past years, if they had no family to take them in, were obliged to retire to the workhouse and be separated from their wives. Since the Great War a small development of council houses has been constructed in our village and several of them are occupied by men retired from the land. The problem is, of course, that there is a waiting list – a situation replicated in local-authority dwellings elsewhere.

David and I resolve to let George and his wife remain in their cottage during the course of their lifetimes. It seems fitting for an employee who has given such long service to the farm. This does, however, present us with a difficulty because a new dairyman will require accommodation and we have none left to offer.

It is this predicament which inspires Stella to ask whether she might become the next dairyman – or should I say dairy*woman*? David and I look at each other and come to the conclusion that there is no earthly reason why Stella should not fill this position for she is now fully accomplished with the cows. The only residual problem is that we should need someone to replace Stella, and, without wishing to denigrate my own gender, I find myself wondering whether any man would be prepared to work under a woman in a farming environment unless that woman owned the farm.

While this becomes a topic for conversation amongst the workforce, Bill informs us that Rosie would like to return. Their son, Keith, is now six years old and he has started school. Rosie wishes to work here during school hours. We have to point out that milking times are largely outside this period. Much anguished thought is put into resolving this dilemma. The more David and I wrestle with it, the more we realise that farmer and farmer's wife are going to have to adapt their own work schedules to accommodate Rosie. There is a financial dividend in that, even if we were to pay Stella the same wage as George, Rosie's restricted hours would earn her less than Stella receives now.

To keep the peace we tell Bill that Rosie would be most welcome to return. It is agreed that during school holidays Rosie will bring Keith with her and ensure he does not get up to mischief. It is also decided that Rosie will keep house for us so that neither Stella nor I are bothered with domestic chores during much of the day. Rosie will make the beds and do all the cleaning. She will cook lunch and have everything washed up before she fetches her son from school. When there is little fieldwork to be done, David will assist with all the milking.

During busy periods such as haymaking, harvest and crop sowing I shall help Stella with morning and afternoon milking and undertake my fairly short milk round during the interim. It is agreed that the remainder of the workforce will muck in as required, and that includes Rosie. All this sounds onerous and perhaps a little chaotic. I just hope that between us we can get the work done without anyone feeling too put upon.

George has given us a month's notice and he will retire on 10 November. I am feeling somewhat concerned as to how his departure will impact upon David and me. We shall both find ourselves with more responsibility at different times of the year. I do not relish early morning milking, and neither does my husband, but the farm must come first.

Clara has left everything to David in her will. Ownership of the farm, therefore, is no longer shared with a third party and the small weekly allowance we gave her in return for her investment in the business is now a saving. Clara was very frugal. Despite her purchases pursuant to the installation of electricity, she had savings amounting to £120.

Clara's legacy and the savings to be made through George's retirement have prompted us to replace our two Ford Model A vans with Model Ys, thereby giving us three quite modern vehicles. David tells me that even the Model Y went out of production last year, but there are so many of these about that spare parts should be available for several years to come. Even the latest model of Ford van only seems to differ from ours by the body shape. The mechanical aspects are almost identical. The main reason for our investment paints a gloomy picture. David is concerned that, in the event of war, replacement vehicles may be hard to come by, so we have adopted a cautionary approach.

I decide that the only way to cheer up is by organising the best Christmas we have ever had. Remembering the disappointments of last year, when Lilian and Dotty were otherwise engaged, I telephone them both during October in the hope they have not made alternative plans. I am delighted to learn that they will be joining us. In a fit of bonhomie I then ring the Harrington-Scotts, and, as an inducement, I mention that the famous Lilian Cairns will be coming. It works, and I am flattered by Isabelle's excited voice at the other end when she tells me how marvellous last Christmas was at Vine's Farm.

In my own excitement at the way plans for the festive season are progressing, I realise suddenly that we have an accommodation problem. Despite having Clara's old bedroom available and Harriet doubling up with Becky, we are one room short. The only solution which comes to mind is that Lilian will have to sleep at her own Honeysuckle Cottage. Sheepishly, I telephone Lilian and explain that I am red with embarrassment, wearing sackcloth and ashes and eating a liberal helping of humble pie. She shrieks with laughter and points out that even if I were doing any of these things, it would impress her not one bit since she cannot see me while we are having a telephone conversation! Dear Lilian, there is no side to her celebrity; and she advises me that If I am going to invite any further guests, then I had better direct them to Honeysuckle Cottage.

I certainly have the bit between my teeth, but deem it expedient to restrict additional invitations to people who live locally. My parents and brother will be here and the Claxtons next door have agreed to come. At this point I begin to wonder whether we shall all be able to sit at the same table for lunch. Both our dining-room and kitchen tables are too small and, in any event, the latter is required for preparing meals.

David comes to the rescue by saying that he can extend the dining-room table in both directions by nailing together some wooden boxes. I fear that this will look rather rough and ready, but he opines that no one will notice once a cloth has been draped over the whole surface. I tell him that we have no tablecloth big enough, so he suggests a bed sheet, or two bed sheets, or however many bed sheets it takes to disguise the timbered crudities below. I think we have a solution.

On the day George Akehurst retires we learn from the wireless that shocking events have taken place in Germany during the night. Ever since the Nazis came to power nearly six years ago the Jewish population there has been persecuted. Hitler blames the Jews for his country's defeat in 1918. I rather think, however, that Britain and her Allies had something to do with the outcome of the Great War. How on earth can German Jews be responsible? Many of them fought for their fatherland. I suppose this is how dictators like Hitler court popularity: find a defenceless minority and unite everyone else against it. One can draw a parallel with the school bully who picks on a weak pupil and encourages others to follow suit. It is both despicable and cowardly.

A Jewish man had killed a Nazi diplomat in Paris, and this act was all the excuse Hitler's thugs needed to rampage through the streets of German cities, smashing windows of Jewish shops and looting their contents. Synagogues similarly were attacked and even burnt to the ground. Anti-Semitic slogans have been daubed on premises, and Jews have been beaten and even killed. This news makes me feel sick, and it takes me back to the last war, when businesses thought to be owned by people of German descent were smashed in this country and dachshunds kicked in the street. A mob is a fearsome thing no matter where it goes about its violent activities.

We learn soon that the night of 9/10 November has been dubbed Kristallnacht owing to the pavements being carpeted in shards of glass from broken windows. The world is not a happy place, and I fear it may become yet unhappier.

On 15 November a delegation of British Jewish and Quaker leaders appeals to the Prime Minister, Neville Chamberlain, requesting the government to permit temporary admission of unaccompanied Jewish children under threat from the Nazis.

The Cabinet debates these proposals on the following day and it prepares a bill to present to Parliament. The bill states that the Government will waive certain immigration requirements, thereby allowing the entry into Britain of unaccompanied children below the age of seventeen, including infants.

On 20 November the Home Secretary, Sir Samuel Hoare, meets a large delegation of Jewish, Quaker and other Gentile groups supporting the cause of refugees. These groups are allied into an organisation called the Movement for the Care of Children from Germany. Sir Samuel agrees to accelerate the immigration process by issuing travel documents on a group basis instead of by individual applications. The Movement promises to find homes for all children arriving and to fund the whole operation so that no burden falls upon the taxpayer. Each child is to have a £50 bond to defray the cost of eventual repatriation once the crisis is over. The next day there is a major refugee debate in the House of Commons and the bill soon passes into law.

On 25 November David and I sit down to listen to the wireless. On the Home Service of the BBC we hear an appeal from the former leader of the Liberal Party, Herbert Samuel, last year elevated to the House of Lords as Viscount Samuel. He is asking British people to offer foster homes for German refugee children. David and I look at each other.

"I know what you're thinking," he says.

"What am I thinking?" I return, as though unable to comprehend his reasoning.

"You're thinking that if this country had been taken over by the Nazis and we were Jewish, then you'd want some kind family overseas to offer sanctuary to Becky. I don't include James because he had his seventeenth birthday earlier this month, which makes the situation all the more poignant, does it not?"

So it is true, then: after nearly twenty years of marriage my husband can read me like a book. If this is a mark of our enduring love for each other, then I am content.

"How many could we take?" I enquire at length.

"No more than three," suggests David, "bearing in mind that we have two children of our own."

"Three, then?"

"Three."

So three it is, and within a short period our home becomes one of some 500 others in Britain offering to take refugees. The Movement for the Care of Children from Germany is soon renamed the Refugee Children's Movement (RCM), and its volunteers begin to inspect the homes of those of us who have offered to foster. We receive our inspection on 16 December, exactly a fortnight after the first party of nearly 200 refugee children arrive in our country. They came from a Berlin orphanage which had been destroyed during the Kristallnacht pogrom. Priority is being given to children who are homeless, orphans or whose parents are in concentration camps or otherwise unable to support them.

Inspections of British homes are not particularly comprehensive, and there is no insistence that ones destined for Jewish children should be Jewish. It is sufficient that houses look clean and families appear respectable. At Vine's Farm we pass the test, which is conducted by a very pleasant Quaker lady who tells us to expect further information early in the new year.

I try to forget tragic events for the time being because Christmas is almost upon us and I am looking forward to having a house full of friends.

My positive expectations are fulfilled even as our guests arrive, for they are obviously in high spirits. A cynic might ascribe their demeanour to an absolute belief in the efficacy of Neville Chamberlain's piece of paper, but I prefer to think that everyone is determined to have a good time no matter what.

Lilian is between jobs – or 'resting', as the acting profession prefers to call such a hiatus – and thus she is more than enthusiastic about entertaining us. It is on Christmas Day, when the house is at its fullest, that Lilian pulls out all the stops. Irrespective of how bloated we must all feel after a gargantuan lunch, Lilian remains her ebullient self, ready to take her audience by storm. She really needs a full orchestra, yet has to make do with me at the piano. She blasts us into party mood with a thundering rendition of George Gershwin's 'I Got Rhythm', from the musical *Girl Crazy*. I can barely keep up with her. Having secured our undivided attention and admiration, she then puts us into more reflective mood by staying with Gershwin and singing that beautiful song

'Summertime', from *Porgy and Bess*. What a tragedy that Gershwin was taken from us last year through a brain tumour! How much more of his genius might we have enjoyed?

For a single lady, Lilian is remarkably good with children, and she has spent the last day or so coaching our three juveniles into the world of entertainment. The piano lessons inflicted upon my daughter by Endacott and me are about to come under scrutiny. With great concentration and determination Becky plays a verse from 'Away in a Manger'. Mercifully she achieves this without error, although her performance would have benefitted from a little acceleration.

If James and the usually shy Harriet think they are going to escape, then they have reckoned without 'Auntie' Lilian. James has learnt no instrument and his voice has broken, so he is spared anything musical. Instead he has been tasked with reading Rudyard Kipling's poem 'If'. He does this with a fluency one might expect from a boy receiving a public-school education, but I detect an element of polish which was surely put there by Lilian. Harriet has learnt to play the recorder at school, and, despite looking a little nervous, she gives us a faultless rendition of a verse from 'Once in Royal David's City'. I notice out of the corner of my eye that Isabelle is visibly moved by her daughter's performance.

Becky then joins Harriet, and the two girls sing unaccompanied the first and last verses of 'In the Bleak Mid-Winter'. I know they are both members of the Endacott choir, but I was unaware they could perform a duet so competently. The only assistance they receive is from Lilian, who gives them the signal to start.

Mr Claxton reads a passage from Charles Dickens' *A Christmas Carol* and Lilian winds up the afternoon entertainment by singing that haunting number 'September Song' to my piano accompaniment. I suspect there may be more performances during the evening, but for the moment I am content to look about the room and see nice people enjoying themselves. Who needs excess alcohol to enliven spirits when one has good company amongst whom are those able to entertain us? Truly, this is already proving to be a remarkable Christmas.

At teatime, however, Lilian tells me that she fears her star is waning in the professional firmament.

"The life of an actress or female singer can be cruelly short, darling," she laments. "You know you're on the way down when someone asks you to play the nurse in *Romeo and Juliet* instead of the girl in the title. Nobody has asked me to play the nurse yet, but I shall never get to play Juliet again – that's for sure."

This causes me to reflect upon the fact that Lilian, Dotty and I are approaching our thirty-ninth birthdays. In little more than a year we shall be classified as middle-aged – help!

CHAPTER 26

A PLACE OF REFUGE

I am delighted to say that both my son and daughter are fully behind the decision to offer Vine's Farm as a foster-home for three German refugee children. I did wonder whether James and Becky might see them as rivals for David's and my affection. Perhaps I should have known my offspring better, for the anticipated arrival of additions to our household is a subject of much excitement.

James is now seventeen and a sixth-former at his school. He lets it be known that his toys of past years may be passed on to our new guests. Some of these playthings have already been given to Rosie's son, Keith, but as he is only six my son's collection remains largely intact. Becky, too, is rummaging through books and dolls which she has outgrown to see what might be appreciated by children who may have to leave most of their possessions in Germany.

Of course I have no way of knowing at this juncture whether we shall be fostering boys or girls, and they could be any age below seventeen.

1939 dawns and my own children will shortly be returning to boarding school. Both James and Becky are hoping our refugees will arrive before the new term begins; otherwise it will be Easter before they all meet. There are no half-term holidays at Endacott or my son's school, but the three seasonal breaks are longer than those enjoyed by children educated through the local authority system. James and Becky have one further week remaining of their current vacation and they keep asking me whether I have heard anything from the RCM.

On 3 January David and I receive a letter requesting one or both of us to travel to Liverpool Street Station in London on the 5th to meet our new charges. We are to look after three sisters – Gretel, Gretchen and Gerda Hubermann, aged thirteen, nine and seven. The letter makes difficult reading. Their father was a music professor at a conservatoire in Berlin who was removed from his post because he is a Jew. When he protested he was thrown into Dachau concentration camp as an enemy of the state. On Kristallnacht their home was broken into by men claiming to be the Gestapo, who stole anything of value they could find. Frau Hubermann has had a mental breakdown and she is unable to care for her daughters. All this brings tears to my eyes, and I feel that I want to hug these three girls at this very moment. I show the letter to my two children, who are profoundly shocked by what they read.

"We're doing the right thing, aren't we, Mummy?" asks Becky.

"Yes, of course we are, darling."

"It's a bit short notice," declares my husband.

"I think it must be something of an emergency," I suggest. "They need to get these children out quickly because there's no one to look after them."

"I'd say they need to get them out before it's too late," David adds.

"Do you think there's going to be another war, then, Father?" enquires James.

"It looks as though there's a war going on inside Germany right now, young man."

On the following day we receive a telephone call from the RCM asking whether we have received their letter and if we could confirm that we will be at Liverpool Street tomorrow morning. David will be busy helping Stella with milking, so I say that I shall be coming alone.

I arrange for my father to drive me to our local station. He tells me to telephone him from London so that he will know what time to collect the three girls and me during the afternoon.

I have not travelled by train for several years and the

experience locally is a much changed one. In 1935 the rail lines were electrified, so gone is the once familiar steam locomotive. At the head of the train is a carriage with two windows at the front for the driver to see through. All rolling stock is finished in green Southern Railway livery, and the whole system is known as Southern Electric. I have to change trains to connect with the fast service to Victoria, where the busy concourse leaves me in no doubt that I am a country person wholly unused to city life.

Unfamiliar experience of the London Underground lends itself to a feeling of insecurity. While I try to ensure that I am going in the right direction, I sense my presence is an inconvenience to everyone else. I just hope that I do not end in an entirely wrong part of the metropolis.

More by good luck than judgment I arrive at Liverpool Street and climb the steps to the mainline station operated by the London and North Eastern Railway.

A glance at my watch indicates that I am early. I can see no gathering of children anywhere. I am unsure what to do next, but, casting my eyes left and right, I notice a group of ladies wearing armbands. Wandering in their direction, I am relieved that each armband displays the letters 'RCM'. I make myself known, and a lady holding a clipboard examines her list of names.

"Ah, yes, Mrs Vera Coulthurst, you're taking three sisters."

"That's correct."

"It's very good of you to have them all. Most people can only take one or perhaps two children. We wouldn't want to split these three up."

"The thought horrifies me."

"Yes, but you see, Mrs Coulthurst, in situations like this we can only do our best. The children have already docked at Harwich, but their train hasn't come in yet. If you stay with us, we'll try to get you sorted out first."

I wait nervously. The rush hour is now over and the station does not look busy by London standards. The railway tracks here are not electrified and I discern the familiar sounds of steam locomotives.

More adults arrive and seek out the women with armbands. We are quite a gathering now, and there is much chatter about how one is going to deal with the language problem. A few days ago I went to our local market town and bought a German phrase book and English/German dictionary. The shop assistant gave me an old-fashioned look, as though I was training to be a Nazi spy!

Mercifully, the RCM lady with whom I spoke earlier has remained close to me. She consults her watch and peers up at the station clock.

"If the train's on time, it should be here any minute," she remarks.

We continue to wait, and every second seems like an eternity. Then suddenly there is a hive of activity in the distance. A train has arrived and is disgorging a large number of people, most of whom are children. There appears to be some confusion as they do not seem to know where to go. Eventually, a handful of adults gesture them to follow.

I am not quite prepared for what I am now seeing. There are children of all ages, looking bewildered and even a little frightened. Toddlers are being led by the hand by older children and some of the older girls are cradling babies in their arms. Everyone looks tired. Each child has a small suitcase and no other luggage.

"Where are the mothers of those babies?" I enquire with anguish.

"In Germany," I am told.

"But why can't their mothers travel with them?"

"No country will take them – not even this one. Only children under seventeen! The only Jewish adults getting out of Germany are those with money, passports and somewhere specific to go."

"But those babies need their mothers," I protest.

"The world doesn't want to know. As far as the mothers are concerned, they're saving their children's lives."

I am distraught. I learn then that these children are the lucky ones, because each already has a foster home allocated. There are others who have been transferred to summer holiday camps being used as temporary holding centres.

The children are paraded in front of us. Each one has, hung around the neck, an identity tag with a three-digit number. They look like auction lots for which we have to bid. I am upset. Perhaps I should not be because I do not doubt that the best is being done for them in extremely difficult circumstances; yet were Britain like Germany, and I saw James and Becky in this miserable state, then I could not bear it.

The RCM lady to whom I first spoke tries to process matters to my advantage. She is not a German speaker, but she has learnt a bare minimum number of words to help herself in the discharge of her duties.

"*Achtung, Kinder!*"

The children are silent.

"*Gretel Hubermann?*"

"*Ja.*"

"*Kommen Sie hier, bitte.*"

The interchange is repeated for Gretchen and Gerda, and very soon I am confronted with three pairs of brown eyes staring hopefully in my direction. I notice that seven-year-old Gerda is hiding something behind a long and rather voluminous overcoat. I smile and point as though to encourage her to reveal the secret. She seems to trust me, and produces a violin case.

"I don't know how she got away with that," remarks the RCM lady. "The Nazis said only one small suitcase. If they'd found it, she probably wouldn't have been able to come here."

I am told the children have been travelling for three days. They were in a sealed train from Berlin to the Hook of Holland. A ferry then took them across the North Sea to Harwich, from where a train brought them to London. I am asked to sign for the three girls, whereupon they become my responsibility.

"*Ich bien Frau Coulthurst,*" I tell them in a not very convincing accent.

"*Guten Morgen, Frau Coulthurst,*" chorus the sisters.

They look hungry as well as tired. My German is not up to

asking them whether they would like something to eat, so I put a finger to my mouth.

"*Essen?*" I enquire.

"*Ja, ja, ja.*"

I detect three attempts to smile.

"*Kommen Sie.*"

I lead them in the direction of a cafeteria. I have in mind a cup of coffee and a sticky bun, but I see little Gerda looking lovingly at something more substantial. A cottage pie has caught her eye. I point to it.

"*Das?*"

"*Bitte*," she responds.

When I ask Gretel and Gretchen, they follow their youngest sister's example. So large helpings of pie are ladled on to four plates and, by popular request, augmented by chips. We sit down to this repast with something to drink: coffee for me and orange juice for my new charges.

Although their table manners are good, the girls devour the meal far more quickly than I could contemplate. While they wait for me to finish I am conscious of their forlorn observation of their empty plates and their envious glances at mine. It must seem an eternity to them before I lay down my knife and fork, whereupon those six brown eyes are once again fixed firmly in my direction. I am familiar with these expressions. They are not dissimilar to that doleful look which Rufus the Second, our cocker spaniel, gives me when I am in the kitchen and he believes it is his supper time. My German is so inadequate that I reach hurriedly for my dictionary and flick through the pages to find the word for 'again'.

"*Wieder?*" I enquire almost triumphantly as I point to the girls' plates and to other customers queuing at the counter with trays yet unfilled.

"*Ja!*" is the eager response accompanied by heads nodding frantically and smiles which engender a warmth within me.

So I purchase three more helpings of cottage pie with chips and add a bread roll for each girl. I cannot possibly eat anything else and therefore content myself with a second cup of coffee. I regard my largess as a sound investment as the girls seem to have relaxed since receiving sustenance and they appear happy in my company. When they have almost licked their plates clean I point to my watch to indicate that we should leave. A further recourse to my dictionary leads to verbal reinforcement.

"*Untergrundbahn.*"

So to the Underground we descend. Were I Lilian or Dotty I should not hesitate to summon a cab, but my humble budget does not run to such luxuries. I am not looking forward to renegotiating the labyrinthine, subterranean transport system with the added problem of not losing my young companions. I get them to link hands and then I take the hand of Gerda.

Mercifully, we arrive at Victoria unscathed, and it is at this juncture that I deem it wise to ask whether the girls need the ladies' convenience. It being anything but convenient to consult my dictionary on a busy concourse, I merely point in the right direction and they follow me. Once inside, I display an element of preparation made for this excursion to the capital. I produce four pennies and proceed to educate my foreign guests into the concept of 'spending a penny'. I hold up one of the coins.

"*Ein* penny – one penny."

I then read "One penny" from the brass lock on one of the doors. I insert the coin in the slot, turn the handle and – hey presto! – the door can be opened. This cubicle is for little Gerda. I see whether Gretchen can repeat this process for herself. She can. Predictably therefore, Gretel has no difficulty and we have achieved success.

When we have all re-emerged I get them to follow my example in the matter of hand washing. Ensuring everyone has their luggage, I proceed to purchase three single tickets before we consult the travel indicator board to determine which platform we require for our homeward journey. I then remember that I must telephone my father.

"*Fernsprecher,*" I explain while secretly congratulating myself for recollecting the word.

My confidence, however, is somewhat curtailed as I detect an element of suppressed humour at my pronunciation. The girls wait patiently outside the telephone kiosk while I speak to my father.

"Yes, Poppa, they're here. We're waving to each other now."

I feel reassured having spoken to him. I suppose it is the little girl coming out in me. How lucky I am to have a father whom I can contact when I wish! With me are three girls much my junior who are not so fortunate.

We find an empty compartment on the corridor train and I feel the more difficult tasks of the day have been completed. The train moves off and no other passengers have joined us. The girls are eagerly looking out of the windows, watching the Victorian houses of South London pass by.

Two young men enter our compartment at East Croydon. My charges are busily chatting away in German, and I notice that the new arrivals are somewhat unsettled by this.

"I thought we beat this lot in the war," says one in a voice deliberately loud enough for us all to hear clearly.

"I suppose we've been invaded too now," comments the other.

The men maintain an unpleasant discourse, made all the more amusing to them by the fact that Gretel, Gretchen and Gerda seem blissfully unaware of its vitriol. Quite what category these oafs place me in is uncertain as I have remained silent. The longer I keep my own counsel, however, the more vituperative their conversation becomes.

"This country's become a dumping ground for foreigners. It's been going on for years. During the war it was the Belgians; now it's the Krauts."

"Yeah, and Jewish Krauts at that."

"They've got a bloody cheek if you ask me."

"Well, no one's asking you!" I snap, unable to contain my anger any longer.

"Oh, it speaks."

The two men begin to laugh raucously.

"If you can't behave yourselves, why don't you go and sit

somewhere else? I don't want to hear any more of your vile talk."

"We don't want to."

"Well, I want you to, so go!"

"What if we stay here?"

"Suppose I pull the communication cord and complain that you are molesting me?"

"You'd get a £5 fine for improper use. Look – it says so on that notice."

"Would the guard believe you rather than me? I've got three witnesses here."

"They can't speak English."

"How do you know?"

"Well, come on, then, little Jew Krauts – say something in English."

The girls are now clearly showing distress. I stand up and with difficulty maintain my balance against the swaying of the train. I reach for the communication cord.

"Do you wish to gamble I won't pull it? You'll be thrown off and probably arrested for assault."

The bravado shown hitherto begins to evaporate.

"Who wants to travel with your sort anyway?"

"Yeah, we're going where the air smells sweeter."

Both men slouch out of the compartment and make a rude gesture as they depart. I return to my seat and, for the sake of the girls, try to quench my anger as quickly as possible. I force a smile in their direction.

Gretel points towards the corridor.

"*Nazis*," she declares.

"*Nein, Liebling*," I answer reassuringly, "*Dummkopfen!*"

The four of us smile and then break into laughter. It is the first time that I have heard them laugh, and it makes me feel wonderful.

We change trains further down the line before alighting at our local station, where my father is waiting with his car.

"*Mein Vater*," I explain.

Dearest Poppa is such a welcoming figure that I can tell the girls have taken an instant liking to him.

"*Willkommen*," he says, holding out his hand. "And I'm afraid that's the only German word I know."

We drive to Vine's Farm, where Rosie has laid out the tea table before leaving to collect Keith from school. James and Becky are in the house and, despite the language barrier, make it clear how pleased they are to receive the new arrivals.

We have crammed three single beds into one room for the time being, thinking that Gretel, Gretchen and Gerda might feel happier if they are together during the early part of their stay. My own children carry their small amount of luggage upstairs and then shower them with offers of their own cast-off books and toys. The three girls are visibly delighted as all their playthings have been left behind in Germany. There is much sorting of this and that, and little Gerda cuddles Becky's once favourite teddy bear as though it must now become a constant companion. I am almost moved to tears.

Later my husband, David, returns from his work on the farm and there follows another round of introductions. As he and I lie in bed that night I ask him whether he thinks we have done the right thing in providing a foster-home for the three refugees.

"Of course we have," he declares. "You cannot doubt it."

Then I tell him of the incident on the train.

"Darling," he concludes, "if, heaven forbid, there is another war, those two idiots will probably have to fight in it and then they'll grow up."

CHAPTER 27

DOING OUR BIT

James and Becky have returned now to boarding school and I am left with the problem of arranging education for our three new additions to the family. David and I have no money for school fees, so I suppose we shall have to try to place Gretel, Gretchen and Gerda in our local council-funded facility. Given their lack of English, this is a daunting prospect for them.

It is a great relief, however, that the girls have come to us in January, while the farm is in its slackest period. With no field work possible on our wet clay soil, both David and Bill between them are able to assist Stella in the dairy and undertake my milk round. This leaves me free to look after the girls and familiarise them with their new surroundings.

All the clothes which Becky has grown out of are distributed as appropriate to our new charges, but their wardrobes are still in need of supplementation. We therefore journey one day to the local market town, where their outfits are completed, including dungarees and wellington boots for walking about the farm.

The girls appear keen to make some contribution towards our work, so I show them how to collect eggs from our folded poultry and grade them according to size. It is not a long job at this time of year as the hens do not lay so well during winter and we often have difficulty in satisfying customer demand. Our refugees become proficient at these tasks and also learn how to move the wheeled henhouses on to fresh grass each day, whereby the pasture becomes suitably manured.

One morning, once these daily undertakings with the poultry

have been completed, we repair to the farmhouse for a cup of coffee. When I look for Gretel I find her in the parlour staring wistfully at our piano.

"Can you play?" I ask her, and, in the light of her lack of English and my lack of German, I point to her and then to the instrument. She nods her head.

"*Ja.*"

I open the keyboard lid and invite Gretel to show me. She points to the sheet-music frame. I open the piano stool and pull out what is lying on the top. It is the music for 'September Song', left over from Christmas when I played and Lilian sang. I place the music in the frame and indicate for Gretel to sit down.

I leave her for a minute or so while I go to fetch her coffee. It is not long before I discern that beautiful and haunting melody emanating from the parlour. It brings everyone in the house – Rosie, Gretchen, Gerda and I – hurrying to the room, all thoughts of coffee seemingly abandoned. I think Rosie is about to cry. I thought that I could play reasonably well, yet by comparison with Gretel my efforts can be classified as somewhat agricultural. She has the most wonderful touch. Her fingers seem to caress the keys as though they are as precious as the music they produce.

"I didn't know that old piano could sound so marvellous," I whisper to Rosie.

When Gretel has finished we all applaud enthusiastically. I kiss her and give her a hug.

"*Das gut. Ist wunderbar!*" I exclaim.

Gretel points to Gretchen.

"Do you play also, Gretchen?" I enquire, pointing to the piano.

She puts her thumb and forefinger close together to indicate that she can play a little, and then points towards her mouth.

"Sing? You can sing?"

"*Singen, ja. Gretel, 'Stille Nacht', bitte.*"

Without sheet music, Gretel plays 'Silent Night' and Gretchen produces an instant lump in my throat with an awe-inspiring rendition of this lovely carol. How we should have adored her presence here at Christmas. Her control is redolent of Lilian as I knew her at Endacott.

I scarcely dare to think what little Gerda can do, but, in the knowledge that she managed bravely to smuggle her violin case out of Germany under the noses of the Nazis, I must find out. So I use my arms to imitate the playing of her instrument, which prompts her to run upstairs and return with it. She asks for no sheet music, but launches into what I believe must be one of the most difficult violin pieces: Pablo de Sarasate's 'Zigeunerweisen'. I am riveted to the spot at the sight of this diminutive figure, almost dwarfed by her instrument, giving a faultless performance with such brio.

David and I often refer to our new guests as the Three Gs, which could mean the Three Girls, but to us denotes Gretel, Gretchen and Gerda. Perhaps we should regard them as the Three Geniuses, for that is what they are surely. They have communicated fluently to Rosie and me through the international language of music, and, despite everything they have suffered, they look upon us now with beaming smiles.

So that is what music can do, and, notwithstanding its beauty and inspiration, I am faced now with something of a dilemma. These girls are so extraordinarily talented that I cannot allow their skills to be neglected. What am I to do?

Almost in desperation I telephone Lilian, explain what has happened and ask when she is likely to stay at Honeysuckle Cottage. To my relief she tells me that she can drive down next weekend. In my excitement I ring Dotty also and ask whether she and Henry would like to visit at the same time. Henry, alas, is busy at work, but Dotty is eager to meet the Three Gs and she agrees to come by train provided I collect her from the station.

So it comes to pass that I am reunited once again with my two old school friends. Three young ladies therefore give three older ones an exhibition of their musical abilities, which reduces Dotty to tears.

Lilian maintains a less emotional stance before declaring,

"These girls are all of a professional standard, but their talent needs to be nurtured."

Of course I am pleased that they have passed the Lilian test, but I remain at a complete loss as to what I should do next.

"There's only one thing for it, Vera," asserts Lilian: "they must go to Endacott. The music department there is stronger than ever, and it wasn't exactly weak in our day. Moreover, the school now offers German as a foreign language, which will help them to learn English."

"Lilian," I respond, "I should love them to go to our alma mater, but it is well beyond David's and my pocket. Not even my father could countenance such an expense, particularly now that he's retired. There are very few bursaries and certainly none for refugees."

"Don't worry about it. With your permission I'll put them through Endacott myself. I can easily afford it."

"I can't possibly ask you to do that."

"You don't have to. Besides, how can you sensibly send them to the local school? The leaving age is fourteen and Gretel is already thirteen.

All three girls need a good education through to eighteen, just like we had. Surely you can't deny them that?"

"I shouldn't want to deny them anything, Lilian, but we don't know how long they're even going to be in this country. They're only supposed to be here until the crisis in Germany is over."

Dotty enters the conversation: "From what I see on my television screen, hear on my wireless and read in the newspapers, I can't see any end in sight regarding the crisis. The Nazis hate the Jews, and as long as Hitler's in power the persecution will continue. Henry fully agrees with me."

"What is television like?" I ask naively, as though to give myself thinking time.

"Oh, it's quite a novelty," answers Dotty, "isn't it, Lilian?"

"Er, yes," Lilian replies in a rather distracted way.

"Did you know," Dotty continues, "there's an announcer called Jasmine Bligh who's a direct descendant of Captain

Bligh. Did you see him played by Charles Laughton in the film *Mutiny on the Bounty?*"

"No," I confess.

"What a pity you can't have television down here in Sussex!" laments Dotty.

"It wouldn't matter if we could," I grumble. "We could never afford it."

"This isn't getting us anywhere," interjects Lilian. "The point is, Vera, these girls could be here for years, and we have no right to hold back their futures."

"You're correct, of course," I concede.

"So you'll consent to my paying the school fees, then?"

"Well . . ."

"Now look, Vera, I don't have any children. I'll never have any children. You'll probably say it's my fault, putting my career before everything, and maybe you're right, but I now have the opportunity to do something positive for these girls. Please don't deny me this chance to help the next generation. Frankly, it would break my heart."

I can see now an expression almost of despair on Lilian's face, and a glance at the girls suggests to me that they know we are talking about them. I feel that I am holding their futures in the palm of my hand.

"Very well, Lilian – it's a wonderful thing you're offering and I gladly accept. I don't doubt for a second that David will agree with me."

"They won't be alone at Endacott," remarks Dotty. "They'll know Becky and her friend Harriet."

"Yes," I concur, "Endacott is the ideal solution."

"I wonder whether I should offer a home for refugees," muses Dotty.

I suspect my friend is brooding over a maternal instinct unfulfilled.

"If you and Henry wish to do so," I comment, "then I see no reason why you shouldn't contact the RCM, but don't imagine you'll end up with a miniature orchestra like David and I have."

"How many do you think we should take? We have a large house."

"It's really up to you and Henry, Dotty. Your house is large, so I shouldn't just have one child; otherwise he or she might feel isolated, particularly if language is a problem. On the other hand, I shouldn't take too many; otherwise you'll never cope. Perhaps two is the ideal number, but make sure you're able to devote the necessary time to them. It's a very big responsibility."

Lilian and Dotty agree to make a long weekend of it so that we may take the Three Gs to Endacott to see whether they like the prospect of being educated there. I telephone the school first thing on Monday morning to explain the situation and to ascertain whether it would be convenient for the headmistress to meet the girls that afternoon. Lilian then comes to the telephone to confirm her defrayment of the fees. The school secretary seems to be rather overawed to find herself speaking to such a public figure and goes to fetch the headmistress – a certain Miss Clayton, who was appointed as Miss Buckmaster's successor.

It transpires that Miss Clayton would be delighted, notwithstanding the short notice, to interview the girls using the German mistress, Miss Haydock, as translator. She would be delighted further if Gerda were to bring her violin. So it is that after an early lunch three Endacott alumnae cram into Lilian's Lagonda with an equal number of potential new girls and set off for this rural seat of learning.

Miss Clayton, desirous of making an impression – particularly in the presence of Lilian, I suspect – has laid on afternoon tea for us. The girls are interviewed separately and they are required also to audition in front of the music mistress.

The headmistress emerges later from her study with my three charges and beams at Lilian, Dotty and me.

"Where did you find such wonderful girls?" she enthuses. "And so gifted! They are a must for the school orchestra and our various productions. They tell me they can all act, play, sing and dance. Miss Haydock says they can converse to an excellent standard in their own language. Of course as a priority they must be taught English, and we shall do that with all celerity. When can they start?"

"How do the girls feel about coming here?" I enquire.

"Oh, they love everything about it. It is like a paradise to them. I believe they're already friends with your daughter, Rebecca, Mrs Coulthurst?"

"Er, yes."

"Capital! I have arranged for Rebecca and her friend Harriet to show them around the school and grounds once they have had some refreshment. Do tuck in now, girls. Then, ladies, perhaps we can have a chat amongst ourselves. Did you know that both Rebecca and Harriet have taken up German with Miss Haydock?"

"Er, no," I confess, a little bewildered.

"Oh, I expect they wanted to keep it a surprise: "*Guten Tag, Mutter*" when you come to collect them at the end of term!" Miss Clayton complements her attempted humour with a shrill little laugh.

"Well," I explain, "Harriet's parents always bring Becky – that is, Rebecca – home for the holidays."

"Oh, yes, of course, you stable Harriet's pony out of term, don't you? How kind! I expect Harriet will be only too pleased to let our German girls have a ride – well, Gretel, anyway. The horse is too big for the other two at present. Now, I understand you three ladies all met at Endacott and have remained firm friends ever since?"

"Yes, absolutely," answers Dotty.

"Then you'll know how happy Gretel, Gretchen and Gerda will be here. The school likes to foster lifelong friendships if it possibly can. If there were more friendship in the world, then we shouldn't have beastly things like wars, should we?"

On that we are agreed. Becky and Harriet arrive with broad grins on their faces. I am unsure whether this demonstrates delight at our presence or at being excused from class. No matter – the five girls depart on the grand tour of Endacott while we from an older generation indulge in further conversation and cucumber sandwiches.

Miss Clayton is effusive in her praise and gratitude towards Lilian for making it possible for my three refugees to attend the school. It is settled that they should start here in a week's time. When the girls return, Miss Haydock is summoned to explain the details to them in German. She also instructs them on how to thank everyone in English. They do it beautifully, and I am almost moved to tears. My only reservation is that I wonder whether circumstances will allow them to complete their schooling here.

On the following Monday I accompany them to Endacott with my father in his car. There remains the problem of school uniform, the wearing of which is rigorously enforced. A school shop has been established where uniforms, which their owners have outgrown, are recycled for the benefit of others. So it is that, before my father and I depart, I get to see Gretel, Gretchen and Gerda proudly kitted out in the livery of my old school. I really must stop wanting to cry.

Now all the children at Vine's Farm are at boarding school, and our house seems so empty with just Stella, David and me in occupation. There is a sadness in our reduction in number which makes a February telephone call from Dotty all the more welcome.

"Vera, you'll never guess what."

"No, Dotty, I suppose I never shall."

"I have two boys!"

In view of Dotty's age and the more advanced years of Henry, not to mention the nine-month human gestation period, no conjecture on my part could possibly have brought me to the conclusion implicit in my friend's declaration.

"You mean Henry's sons by his first marriage?" I enquire, having thought quickly in order to produce an intelligent response.

"No, silly – two boys from Germany on the Kindertransport. That's what everyone's calling the scheme now. I thought at first this meant it was a form of transport that was being kinder to youngsters in distress. Then I discovered that *Kinder* means children in German! Can you imagine?"

"Er, yes."

"Pardon?"

"Nothing, Dotty – go on."

"Well, you were quite right to recommend I should offer to foster two children. You see Josef – that's spelt with a J, but pronounced as a Y – and Dieter are brothers who were terrified of being parted, but I've prevented that from happening."

"Good for you, Dotty."

"Yes, well, I had to laugh when I saw Dieter's name written down before we met, because it's spelt like our word 'dieter', and I thought perhaps he's too fat and needs to go on a diet! The truth is, however, that he's not fat at all – quite slim, in fact, just like his brother."

I have to pause briefly before responding: "Er, how old are they?"

"Josef is sixteen and Dieter fourteen. I suppose they allocated me older boys as I've never brought up children before. Henry wanted to pack them off to boarding school – at his own expense, of course – but I said what's the point of offering a home to children and then getting rid of them as soon as possible? No offence directed at you, Vera, with your three girls. I mean, Endacott's a different kettle of fish as we all know, and they can learn English there and be with Becky and Harriet. Anyway, we've found a marvellous fee-paying day school nearby, so Josef and Dieter have just started there and are very happy. They walk home each day and I have their tea ready for them. Well, my tweeny has, if you know what I mean."

"I'm really very pleased for you, Dotty."

"Well, I like to do my bit."

When I have put the telephone down I try to imagine what a future Christmas might be like at Vine's Farm if David and I were to invite Dotty and her entourage along with all our usual guests. I rather think we should have to prevail upon

Lilian to open up Honeysuckle Cottage as an overflow facility for accommodation. We should be scarcely short of talent for entertainment, and I do wonder whether Josef and Dieter might then reveal that they are adept at tap-dancing, juggling or even ventriloquism!

CHAPTER 28

THE LOST GENERATION REVISITED

Much of nature lies dormant when a new calendar year dawns. One might therefore question when nature's own new year opens its account. I contend that this occurs when rooks start building their nests during mid February. They construct these rookeries with twigs in high trees, such as elms. At this time of year one may cast one's eyes upwards to discern the first twig-bearing rook and any country-dweller does not have to journey far to observe this phenomenon because rookeries are frequently located along roadsides. The rook employs altitude for security and he is not reliant on seclusion or his own aggression.

It is now that I reflect upon verse learnt while studying at Endacott as a girl in my teens:

> Over the land freckled with snow half-thawed
> The speculating rooks at their nests cawed,
> And saw from elm-tops, delicate as flower of grass,
> What we below could not see, Winter pass.

These words were written by Edward Thomas, killed in France in 1917.

Would that man might conduct himself with seasonal predictability as other species, such as the rook, do! Yet he seems incapable – or rather, unwilling. The demise of our quatrain poet tells us all about the worst excesses of mankind.

A renewed fear swept our country in the wake of the Munich Crisis. It was the fear of aerial bombing. No one was sure how we would cope with it. Last November Sir John Anderson was appointed Lord Privy Seal and placed in charge of air-raid precautions (ARP). Expenditure has soared in this regard and plans have been made to evacuate all schoolchildren and mothers with offspring under five from large cities and to billet them in private houses in various 'reception areas'. Arrangements also have been made to provide special trains to facilitate such evacuation. In order to avoid alarm, details of this initiative have been leaked out in a cautious, hesitant way. People seem more complacent now than they were last September, believing in Mr Chamberlain's piece of paper bearing Herr Hitler's signature.

The Führer, however, does not appear finished with Czechoslovakia. Here is a country created out of the northern part of the defeated Austro-Hungarian Empire in the aftermath of the Great War. Weakened and diminished by the Munich Agreement, a hyphen was inserted in its very name during last October. On 15 March this manufactured nation disintegrates. Slovakia becomes an independent state. Without bloodshed the remaining territory becomes a German protectorate. German troops march through Prague and Hitler spends the night there. The policy of appeasement, however, continues.

One wonders what the Führer has to do to provoke a major war in Europe. My husband is convinced that Poland is now the straw which will break the camel's back. David's opinion is strengthened on 31 March by Britain and France issuing a guarantee in support of Polish independence. A triple alliance is drawn up between the three countries. The fear seems to be that if any resistance were raised in Eastern Europe against Germany, then Poland would need to be an element of such resistance. There is therefore a strong desire to prevent Poland siding with the Germans. So our nation has nailed its colours to the mast, but we feel an uneasy tension.

At Vine's Farm the Easter holidays are now upon us and we welcome not the usual two, but five children back into our fold. The Three Gs are speaking a little English, which facilitates our communication. They have taken to our language better than Becky has to German, giving credence to the notion that English people often resort to raising their voices when not understood by foreigners.

Harriet has kindly allowed Gretel to ride her pony while at Endacott and when Eddie is stabled here during vacations. As Miss Clayton suggested, Gretchen and Gerda are not yet sufficiently grown to occupy Eddie's saddle, but they love to help look after him.

I learn that all three girls from the Kindertransport have settled in well at my old school, and they have become extremely popular owing to the novelty of their background and the use to which their talents are being put. Gretel and Gerda are stars of the school orchestra, and Gretchen is a leading light in both drama and singing. Endacott has established a fine reputation for the performing arts, and I can think of no better institution in which to place my new charges.

Alas, the vacation passes all too quickly and the Harrington-Scotts arrive with Harriet to take the five girls and Eddie back to school. The Bentley is a large vehicle, but everyone has to squeeze in and they all wave cheerfully as car and horsebox pull away. It is I who am sad because there is an absence now of the chatter, laughter and enthusiasm which so often accompanies youth. When I collect eggs and move the henhouses I am either alone or with another adult, for whom serious conversation is the norm. On my milk round there is no one occupying the van's passenger seat and no one helping me to carry the crates. I suppose it is just my maternal instinct, experiencing emptiness while bereft of young company.

Scarcely have we chain-harrowed and rolled those pastures laid up for hay before the Minister of Agriculture, Sir Reginald Dorman-Smith, announces a grant of £2 per acre for ploughing up grassland.

"This can mean only one thing," declares David: "the country is preparing for war."

His analysis sends a shiver down my spine, but my head tells me that he is right. Britain cannot feed itself. Our island can produce only about one-third of its needs. Everything else has to be imported, and in wartime that means our merchant ships will have to run the gauntlet of submarines, surface raiders and laid mines. Dairy and meat products require a larger acreage than cereals and vegetables. An acre of grassland feeds one or two people, while an acre of wheat feeds twenty. A similar area of potatoes will feed forty.

The only way therefore to grow the greatest weight of human food per acre is to convert much of our pasture to arable land. The penalty is, of course, that arable crops exhaust the soil whereas fields grazed by livestock build up fertility. The salient question thus arises whether there is sufficient fertility stored in our grassland to produce good crops for the duration of conflict.

We decide to take our hay crop and then plough as much pasture as we dare, consistent with maintaining our dairy herd. If necessary, the beef herd can be sold off. David suggests that if war comes, then much livestock will be culled for human consumption to enable more land to come under the plough. We should like to keep our hens as they occupy only a small area and, like our cows, they contribute to fertilisation. The problem is that chickens consume wheat and this might not be tolerated by the authorities.

It occurs to me that war might signal the end of our livery business. The only horses deemed necessary in any significant quantity during hostilities surely will be those shires required for agricultural purposes. Our farming industry, depressed over the past two decades, has not mechanised so quickly as the army, which will not want the huge number of horses requisitioned during the Great War. The amount of horse-drawn traffic on our streets is now quite small, and I suspect that many of our equine friends will be slaughtered because land cannot be wasted on growing oats other than for human consumption.

No doubt many pets will be culled for the same reason, and it is this thought which causes me to stare at our dear Rufus the Second, who is giving me his usual loving look.

I am not overcome with potential grief, however, for Rufus is a very capable gun dog and can earn his keep through retrieving rabbits whenever David indulges in a little rough shooting. Indeed, it is obvious to me that the feral rabbit will provide a useful food source in wartime for humans as well as satisfying our spaniel's own palate. I believe that rabbit fur also could become a sought-after commodity with which to combat shortages. One might fashion a crude pair of gloves from this material – while they may appear unprepossessing, their primary function of keeping one's hands warm is not in dispute.

Haymaking is an activity which boarding-school children miss, for it coincides with the summer term. So there will be no excited youngsters in the hayfields at Vine's Farm. The job is completed almost with solemnity, and once the crop is ricked and thatched the plough is set to work at a time when traditionally it would lie in the shed.

I sense that social life might be curtailed severely in the months and years ahead, so I feel an urge to extract some joy while we remain at peace. A school reunion is being planned at Endacott towards the end of term. I have not been to one of these occasions since I accompanied Lilian and Dotty there back in 1927. I am determined to go, and when I contact my two old friends I discover that they are both similarly disposed.

So it is that in late July we climb into Lilian's Lagonda and roar off for a day out. I remark that I find it surprising Lilian has not changed her car in so many years. She quips that they are growing old together and have become inseparable. Whatever the truth of this analysis, I can see the sense in not changing a vehicle if the one you drive is still giving good service. In any event, if war comes there will be petrol shortages and many cars will have to be laid up for the duration.

We arrive at Endacott and soon learn why Miss Clayton, the headmistress, has chosen to hold the reunion just before the girls break up for the summer vacation. Not only are girls deployed to act as hostesses and waitresses, but we are treated to entertainment by the school orchestra and choir together with the reading of poetry. An exhibition of paintings by the pupils is on display, and similarly arrayed for our inspection are examples of needlework. A small gymkhana is arranged in which those girls fortunate enough to be accompanied at school by their ponies are able to compete.

All this seems a huge advance on my experience of Endacott more than twenty years ago. I am surprised to meet Lord Cloudsley's daughters, Ladies Clarissa and Constance, who confess that this is the first reunion to which they have ever been. Apparently, curiosity about the school's progress has got the better of them. If I am amazed, then they must be flabbergasted.

Harriet competes in the gymkhana, and she also sings in the choir with Becky. I am proud of them both, and the three Jewish girls entrusted to my charge elicit tears of emotion from me and from others. One can scarcely imagine what they have been through in Germany, yet here they are, the undisputed stars of the afternoon, raising heights of achievement at Endacott to unprecedented levels – unless, perhaps, one includes Lilian! Gretel gives a piano recital, Gretchen sings a solo and little Gerda, a child prodigy if ever I saw one, gives a virtuoso performance on her violin.

As I sit here, listening to this diminutive musician playing like an angel, I vow that I shall do everything in my power to protect these three girls. If war comes, then there will be no prospect in the foreseeable future of their returning to Germany. They will stay at Vine's Farm when not attending school. If anyone from my country dares to declare these innocents are enemy aliens and tries to intern them, then I shall fight to keep them even if I have to declare them farm labourers essential to the war effort. As long as I have breath in my body, and Lilian has money in her pocket, Vine's Farm and Endacott will look after these girls and mould them into three fine ladies who may take their place in a better, future world.

The apparent war footing on which British agriculture has been put – at least by our acceptance of Sir Reginald Dorman-Smith's £2 per acre – has virtually convinced David and me that hostilities could break out at any moment. Many people, however, seem somewhat complacent as Hitler appears to have gone to ground. At least he has not walked into any other countries since March. So Britain carries on as normal. Holidays are taken by the seaside, while cricket and tennis are played as though it is just another summer.

Pessimistically, I regard the Endacott reunion as something of a last hurrah. It is in this mood that my husband and I resolve to have a last hurrah at Vine's Farm in the hope that it will not be a last hurrah. We invite the usual suspects for a short summer vacation, which necessitates Lilian accommodating some of our guests at Honeysuckle Cottage.

This provides an opportunity to meet Josef and Dieter, the two Jewish boys being fostered by Dotty and Henry. They welcome the chance to converse in their native tongue with our three talented refugees, but are sufficiently well mannered to test their limited English when in anyone else's presence.

Everyone seems ecstatically happy, no doubt helped by the glorious August weather. In the harvest fields we have many volunteer hands stooking sheaves between periods of resting in the sun with a picnic. Becky, Harriet and Gretel take turns to ride Eddie while Gretchen and Gerda run about laughing, though there is so much in their lives that might preclude mirth. Lilian is reading a film script. I wonder whether the film will be shot or whether she will be asked to consider performing a propaganda role instead. Round and round goes the binder, with the tractor exuding its familiar scent of vaporising oil. As the standing wheat diminishes, so rabbits relocate themselves towards the centre of the field. When the final cuts are being made the creatures bolt in all directions to find the nearest cover, which must seem a continent away.

"Look!" cries Gretel excitedly. "Nazis! See how they run!"

Everyone laughs – for the moment, at least.

Britain and France have been engaged in diplomatic talks with Soviet Russia. The hope is that an alliance may be forged by which Germany might be dissuaded from invading Poland. The Poles, however, refuse to let the Red Army pass through their country in order to engage the Germans in the event of war. The talks break down on 21 August, and later that day the German Foreign Minister, Joachim von Ribbentrop, is invited to Moscow. On 23 August he and his Soviet counterpart, Vyacheslav Molotov, sign a non-aggression pact. My husband descends into a dark depth of despair.

"What a mess has been made of this!" he declares. "I've always said Danzig with the Polish Corridor was a mistake, and now Hitler's got a passport to seize the lot!"

"What does this mean for us?" I ask, fearing that I know the answer already.

"The blunt truth is this, darling: if Germany invades Poland, we're obliged to come to her defence unless we run away from the guarantee we've given. If we do that, we'll have no credibility left in international affairs, quite apart from the fact that it'll show we have no stomach for a fight."

"David's right," adds Henry. "For the moment we shall just have to hope the Nazis do nothing. If German troops enter Poland, then it's almost certain the balloon will have gone up."

Everybody now is profoundly depressed. It is almost as though we have been fooling ourselves that the problem would go away, and now it seems that peace may be measured in days or weeks rather than months or years.

The holiday for our guests at Vine's Farm comes to an end. Lilian returns to London while Dotty, Henry and their two Jewish boys repair to their house in Surrey. Tarquin and Isabelle return home with Harriet and promise as usual to call for Becky, our three refugees and Eddie in time for the autumn term at Endacott.

At 4.45 a.m. on Friday 1 September, German troops cross the Polish frontier. An hour and a quarter later the Luftwaffe bombs Warsaw. There is no bloodless occupation this time. The Poles appeal to her allies for help. Britain and France appear to fudge the issue, hoping to persuade Hitler to withdraw from Poland, thus preventing a full-scale war.

As a precaution the scheme for the evacuation of younger children from major British cities is swung into action. Primary-school pupils, their teachers and children under five with their mothers qualify for the exodus. The operation is voluntary, and not everyone goes. Primary pupils assemble at their schools and are then taken to railway stations. Tearful mothers wave them farewell.

The evacuees are transported to 'reception centres' in the countryside. Our local centre is the village hall. David and I feel that we must contribute, particularly as we have already three refugees from our potential enemy. With my husband still busily engaged in harvesting, I take one of the milk vans to the hall, where there is feverish activity.

Each evacuee has an identity label tied to his or her lapel, not unlike the Kindertransport children, but there the similarity ends. Whereas the process at Liverpool Street Station was conducted in an orderly fashion, what I see now leaves much to be desired. Some of our local inhabitants are snatching children whom they deem to be the most desirable in terms of attractiveness, attire and cleanliness. I am embarrassed to observe some fellow farmers' wives picking out the older, stronger-looking boys, no doubt with the intention of using even these small specimens as unpaid labour.

I remain passive, not wishing to be part of this unseemly scrum. There is, of course, a residual thought that I might be landed with city children who could be verminous, bed-wetting and not easily adaptable to our way of life; yet there I stand in the background, waiting for the seething mass of humanity to thin out. I know what will happen if there are children left unclaimed once the last local adult has departed. The poor wretches will be taken from house to house in the hope of finding accommodation. I am reminded of that depressing film which Lilian made called *Unwanted*.

Having waited for some twenty minutes, I survey the few remaining children standing forlornly on the bare boards of the village-hall floor. They make a pathetic spectacle, not least because they have been made painfully aware that they lack desirability. The billeting officer, a middle-aged lady, notices me and approaches.

"Oh dear," she begins. "Most people can only take one child, and we have two sisters here who refuse to be parted. They're six-year-old identical twins, very clean, but terrified. You couldn't possibly, could you?"

The two girls are cowering behind other children, which could be another reason why nobody has chosen them. They are identically dressed and I cannot tell them apart. I squat down so that my height is not much greater than theirs.

"Would you both like to come and stay with me? I have a farm with cows, chickens, horses, cats and a lovely dog. Wouldn't you like that?"

"That would be nice, wouldn't it?" adds the billeting officer.

The girls are too frightened to speak, but nod their heads in unison.

So it is that Jean and Joan Garland are added to the personnel at Vine's Farm. They are from Balham in South London. Their father is a police constable. We all make them welcome. David and I now have a family of seven children, six of whom are girls. The local council school is to provide educational facilities for the British evacuees and their teachers. The village hall has been commandeered as an extra classroom.

During the evening I receive a telephone call from Dotty, who appears somewhat alarmed.

"Vera, I've been watching television with Josef and Dieter."

"How nice for you all!" I reply a little wearily. "So what were you watching exactly?"

"A Mickey Mouse cartoon."

I try not to sound like an intellectual snob: "Aren't you a little past that, dear?"

"No – you don't understand. Suddenly the BBC pulled the plug!"

"What do you mean 'pulled the plug'?"

"They stopped broadcasting. The screen went blank. Everything blacked out – no announcement or anything!"

"Are you sure your television receiver hasn't broken down?"

252

"No – there's nothing wrong with it. I checked by ringing a friend who's also got one, and she's found the same thing! Oh dear – you don't think they know there's going to be another war, do you? I mean, there are so few of us who have television and we're all in and around London. If there's a war, television won't be much use in keeping the nation informed. The wireless will do all that."

"I really don't know what to say, Dotty. In any event, there's nothing we can do about it."

"But I've got two Germans in the house!"

"And I've got three. Now, look, Dotty – don't panic. Our German children are Jews who have been persecuted by the Nazis. We have given them refuge and we must look after them with the same kindness we should expect anyone to give British children in similar circumstances. Promise me you'll care for Josef and Dieter no matter what."

"Yes, of course, Vera – I suppose you're right."

At the end of our conversation I put down the telephone with an air of uneasiness.

On Saturday 2 September Britain seems to carry on as usual. There is a full football league programme although it is revealed that attendances are somewhat smaller than expected. Clearly, Dotty is not alone in thinking that something sinister is afoot. The Italian dictator, Mussolini, is reported to be about to propose a conference to discuss events in Poland. Britain insists that Germany must withdraw its invading troops before such a conference can be considered.

During the evening there is an animated debate in the House of Commons. The Prime Minister, Neville Chamberlain, continues to hope that diplomacy will continue, but other voices from both sides of the House believe the time has come to stop pussyfooting around with Hitler. They take the view that an immediate ultimatum should be sent to Berlin. On the following morning Lord Halifax, the Foreign Secretary, arranges for the relevant document to be dispatched.

The British ultimatum is delivered to the German government at 9 a.m. We are told that the Prime Minister will broadcast to the nation at 11.15. At Vine's Farm the household gathers in the parlour and the wireless is switched on. We wait pensively as the valves warm up and transmission begins. At precisely eleven fifteen we hear the grave tones of Neville Chamberlain, who always sounds to me like an undertaker expressing his condolences to a recently bereaved client.

> I am speaking to you from the Cabinet room at 10 Downing Street. This morning the British Ambassador in Berlin handed the German government a final Note stating that, unless we heard from them by eleven o'clock that they were prepared at once to withdraw their troops from Poland, a state of war would exist between us. I have to tell you now that no such undertaking has been received, and that consequently this country is at war with Germany. You can imagine what a bitter blow this is to me. . . .

At this point I leave the room through the French windows and stand alone in the garden to collect my thoughts. There is one person in our parlour for whom I fear more than any other, and he is my son, James. In two months he will be eighteen and of military age. I do not doubt we could get an exemption for him on the grounds that we need him on the farm, but I sense that, like his father and late uncle, he will want to volunteer for military service.

It is now as a mother that I despair. I remember giving birth to him and how proud David was that the Coulthurst name would continue into the next generation. I recollect pushing him in his pram past the field where Lilian and I once entertained convalescing soldiers from the last war; only sheep then safely grazed in a time of hard-won peace. Peace! What price peace now? Must my son – my most beautiful and only son – be swallowed up in the maw of military conflict? I suppose he must, along with many more beautiful sons born of frightened mothers thinking just like I am at this moment.

We of the lost generation have lost again, for we have lost the peace. And what of Vine's Farm, which we have struggled to buy and are still buying? Will some enemy bomber crew, driven from its city targets by British fighter aircraft, discharge their deadly cargo on our humble steading before fleeing like terrified rabbits across the water?

Suddenly, the air-raid siren begins its eerie wailing. It is probably just an exercise to alert us all to the dangers which lie ahead, but it makes no difference. There are no air-raid shelters here. All I can do is cast my eyes to the heavens and hope.